The Heart of Healing

"Very educational and informative. I believe this resource will help many. *The Heart of Healing* is thought-provoking, i.e., "maybe that would help me." Explanations are easy to understand and follow for people not in the medical field. My personal favorite was the B-M-W—I am already trying it for migraine issues. Thank you!"

—Kathy D.

"In this culture, people tend to specialize in distinct aspects of health care. *The Heart of Healing* is unique in showing how God created our physical bodies, spirits, minds, and emotions to be integrated to make up who we are. To be completely healthy and whole, we must attend to all these parts of our being and understand God's plan for all these aspects of ourselves."

—Joyanne B.

"Bonnie combines spiritual depth, biblical wisdom, deep compassion, and extensive experience in strengthening and pain relief. I especially appreciate her practical, effective, and comprehensive approach to healing."

—Dr. D. Richard Ferguson—author,
Food for Your Soul podcast

"Bonnie shares practical tools for the total healing of the whole person. Her process reveals how to prevent and resolve common physical pain that often results from deeper internal pain."

—Kary Oberbrunner, author of *Unhackable,*
Elixir Project Experience, and Your Secret Name

"Let Bonnie Yost's book, *The Heart of Healing*, introduce you to *The God Who Heals* and to the physical therapist author whose message leads you to the healing you and others seek. After nearly forty years as lead pastor in local churches and now a Breakthrough Coach and Pastor to Leaders in the global marketplace, I know this is the book I have sought for myself and others. It integrates the healing of body-soul-mind-spirit as God intended and created us. To know and value Bonnie's uniqueness, let this treasure-box of truth and wisdom take you into her website where her virtual teaching will take you to deeper levels of understanding of healing. A conversation with Bonnie is coaching at its best—someone who can ask you the right questions to reveal the right answers to you, so you are empowered to act on them in partnership with God. I am exceedingly grateful to God for Bonnie's impact on my life, which I will carry everywhere I go!"

—Mark A. Williams,
Coach-Mentor-Pastor-Teacher-Author

4x4 Healing Commendations

Early in my career, I realized the need for a treatment approach that cares for the body (physical pain and problems), the heart (emotional trauma), the mind (thinking patterns and problems), and the spirit (belief system and values). I developed *4x4 Healing* to bridge the gaps and offer comprehensive treatment. Here are a few testimonies from people who have received **4x4 Healing** to move from pain and bondage to healing, freedom, and wholeness.

"Since beginning Christian counseling in 1989, I have used effective materials to bring God's truth to people. I have found, however, that follow-up is needed throughout life. The *4x4 Healing* materials offer excellent tools to accomplish that follow-up and complement counseling and other approaches. I especially like the *Daily 7 R's* and the *Living 7 R's* as life tools. These tools are concrete, easily used, and result in measurable improvement. My clients grow in healthy independence and life-management skills. The personal application and healthy lifestyle building journey help everyone completing *4x4 Healing* to move into the full richness and freedom of life that Christ offers us. *4x4 Healing* materials are versatile—they can be used with individuals, couples, families, and groups. There is enough material to keep a good pace and build an effective, Christ-focused foundation or to take more time and dig deeper into personal needs and issues. These are very interactive and experiential tools that promote renewing our minds and living God's truth. I recommend *4x4 Healing* and the practical tools and materials for every Christian counselor and prayer warrior."
— Kristen Hungerford, MS, LPC, Littleton, CO

"Have you ever met someone who has been raised from the dead? Let me introduce myself! My name is Hope, and I wasn't literally dead, of course. However, mentally and spiritually, I was in the grave. Buried alive, just waiting impatiently for my physical body to join the rest of me in death. My depression and pain caused me to ask God for death, even though I wasn't even sure He existed. I felt hopeless and suicidal.

Relationships and events from my childhood had led me to believe and live lies about myself—that I was unlovable and worthless, an inconvenience and an embarrassment to myself and others, fundamentally and unrecoverably flawed. Since I had been hurt (and in an attempt to alleviate my pain), I permitted myself to do anything I thought would make me feel better. Morality and sinfulness were not considerations, so I heaped guilt and shame on top of my original injuries.

While going through my second divorce, my Father in Heaven reached out from eternity, got my attention, and I accepted Jesus Christ as my Savior. In a long healing and recovery process, He gently and compassionately drew me to Himself, providing what I needed at every step. When I began *4x4 Healing*, I was still deep in isolation and depression, suffering from doubt, and experiencing no joy or security in my salvation. I hadn't been attending church for several years and was losing my faith.

By working with my trained coach, I have come to a place I would never have believed possible. Through the *4x4 Healing* approach, I have realized that my God deeply cares about me and is actively involved in my life. Through Him (using the *4x4 Healing* tools and Biblical teaching), I have received healing, which psychiatrists, counselors, and Twelve-Step work over 35 years could not provide. Jesus is leading me out of the depression and isolation that have plagued me since childhood. I am beginning to feel the joy of my salvation for the first time, and He is leading me into areas of service that I couldn't have imagined.

4x4 Healing depends on the power of the Holy Spirit to guide the healing process. Together, we have torn down many of the painful barriers which blocked my awareness of my Heavenly Father's love for me, and my faith is growing. As that happens, I am experiencing even more supernatural healing only possible through Jesus. In short, I'm in the process of becoming the person God created me to be."

— Hope, Colorado Springs, CO

"The *4x4 Healing* approach to healing the mind, body, soul, and spirit is effective and practical. The group experience is faith-stretching and "body" building while working together in Christ-developed character and unity. I received healing and restoration. The *4x4 Healing Trail Guide* training dramatically changed the way I think about the mind-body connection. This training stretched and changed me. Praise God!"

— Tom Berscheid, MA, LMFT, Wayzata, MN

"I just wanted to call and say thank you to Bonnie. I was listening to the tapes that I bought at the conference after going to her presentation, which triggered a few things. While seeing my second patient today, things weren't making sense. I mentioned that I had been listening to this tape, and she opened up and provided a lot of information that made the physical therapy go better. It helped me treat the patient, and it helped her also. I just wanted to say thank you. Please pass the thank you on to the survivors and counselors who gave of their time and resources. I want them to know that they have helped at least one person. I appreciate it very much. Thank you."

— Sandy Palmer, PT, Dayton, OH

"When I began learning about the spiritual realm, I was 75-years-old. Life presented pain and problems, but I just thought I had to deal with problems and unhappy situations on my own. I prayed mostly for others and didn't think about putting personal situations immediately into God's hands. In going through *4x4 Healing*, I have recognized influences of the flesh, the world, and the enemy, and I can now stand well in the battle without fear. Learning more about who I am in Christ has been a wonderful journey for me, and it will go on through life. This material has helped me examine myself, grow closer to God and others, and feel God's power, love, and joy. He is giving me victory and continually, a more abundant life!"

— Marje, Elizabeth, CO

"I am more than grateful to have learned how to use O-C-A in my life. I was very codependent with my sister and, in some ways, in toxic bondage. I felt like a slave to her needs, like I was the only one that could help her, and that was my duty. Since early childhood, my mother trained me to help her out of all of the messes she got into. Then I learned that I had healthy Options! I found I could consider healthy Options and make Choices that were far more life-giving for me—and in the long run, for my sister. I began to take Action. I still needed some assistance with what it looks like in relationships, so I received coaching through *4x4 Healing*. It became a heart-freeing, joy-filled experience and way of life. It took a lot of weight off my body, soul, and spirit."

— Brenda, Elizabeth, CO

"Although we only did a few small sections of the *4x4 Healing* resources, I learned about how we are following a map (whether we are aware of it or not), and I want to follow God's map. *4x4 Healing* made me very conscious of the places and people I need to avoid to stay on the path God has for me. I now accept Jesus as the only way, and I'm not going to let anyone or anything stand in my path. I've made so many bad choices in my life. I'd need a book to tell you of them all, but that's why I'm in prison now. After answering questions through *4x4 Healing*, I realize that the person standing in my way wasn't another person but was me. Another thing I learned is something so simple. I don't know why I wasn't aware of it. It's that I can lean on God for physical stamina and strength, and emotional and mental strength to overcome pain, anger, resentment, confusion, tension, and irritation. He will help me overcome my tendency to be offended by others, help me through illness, and best of all—Jesus will help me reverse negative thinking about myself, others, and circumstances. I like how *4x4 Healing* showed me how to question myself, instead of trudging along in pain or turmoil. Now I can stop, ask how I'm feeling, take it to God, and He will lift me. Don't get me wrong. I still struggle with problems and painful feelings, but not for long because the Holy Spirit reminds me of what I've learned. In those moments, I am filled with joy, relief, and peace. Thank you for the powerful prayers in *4x4 Healing,* and for helping me and other inmates to know that we matter to you and God."

— Jenny, Denver Department of Corrections inmate

THE HEART OF HEALING

Break Free from Physical Pain
and Emotional Wounds

THE HEART OF HEALING

Break Free from Physical Pain and Emotional Wounds

BONNIE YOST, PT

Published by Author Academy Elite
P.O. Box 43, Powell, OH 43035
www.AuthorAcademyElite.com

Scripture quotations taken from the New American Standard Bible® (NASB), Copyright © 1960, 1962, 1963, 1968, 1971, 1972, 1973, 1975, 1977, 1995 by The Lockman Foundation. Used by permission. www.Lockman.org

Scripture quotations marked NLT are taken from the Holy Bible, New Living Translation, copyright ©1996, 2004, 2007, 2013, 2015 by Tyndale House Foundation. Used by permission of Tyndale House Publishers, Inc., Carol Stream, Illinois 60188. All rights reserved.

Library of Congress Control Number: 2020921539

Softcover: 978-1-64746-587-2
Hardcover: 978-1-64746-588-9
e-Book: 978-1-64746-589-6

Available in hardcover, softcover, e-book, and audiobook.

Any internet addresses, email addresses, and phone numbers in this book are accurate at the time of publication. They are provided as a resource. The author or the publisher do not endorse them or vouch for their content or permanence.

With deepest thanks, I dedicate this book:

to my family
for their patient love and understanding
through this process . . .

to my many wonderful patients
who chose not to "settle," but pressed forward
to be the best they could be and
gave me the privilege to journey with them . . .

to you, the reader—
to heal body, mind, emotions, and spirit,
and to see all the blessing God has for you . . .

and, most of all,
to our Creator, Lord, and Savior, Jesus,
Who provided everything needed to do this work.

TABLE OF CONTENTS

INTRODUCTION

Do you feel a deep yearning in your body and heart for relief from pain?
Does your spirit search for lasting joy, and peace?
Do you think that these hopes are even possible?

The answers to those questions are the *most important* messages of this book.

I want you, the reader, to experience what I and most of my patients have—healing that touches body, mind, emotions, and spirit along with pain relief, deep joy, and peace that overshadow the hurts and trials of life.

Your deep desire for these qualities can become a reality, and you can have confidence that they will last. If that sounds impossible to you, you are not alone.

Certainly, you can make choices, and you can do things toward the goal of having more joy, peace, and pain relief in your life. As I share some of those principles, and as you experience and practice healthy habits presented here, write down where you find and feel increasing pain relief, joy, and peace. Hold tight to that knowledge and watch those dreams come to life.

As a seventy-five-year-old woman, Martha came to me with a painful, debilitating skin rash. The eczema covered much of her body with cracking, weeping, and bleeding sores. She was a Christian and had prayed for healing for years. She shared how she had believed she had healed from past hurts. Through treatment, Martha learned that her mind, emotions, and spirit held wounds that affected how she felt, her beliefs, and her body. The wounds she thought had resolved from childhood abandonment and loss of her father had not healed. Within a year, this precious woman found a more profound knowledge and relationship with her Creator. As residual pain was revealed and attended, her skin healed completely. Through treatment and training, she found deep healing, pain relief, joy, and peace. Martha shared her increasing joy and peace with me and with many others in her life.

Chloe came to see me. She was thirteen-years-old and suffered from stomach aches, digestive problems, and headaches. As we worked together, she said that her dreams of having her pain relieved and living a safe, peaceful, joy-filled life were like "a fairy tale." She couldn't believe it was possible. Eventually, Chloe moved into a safe family situation. As I worked with her and her new family, Chloe learned about safety and good choices. She learned healthy self-care, relational skills, and relaxation practices. Her physical, emotional, mental, and spiritual pain (and wounds) were addressed and given care. Chloe learned that her hopes of pain relief, joy, and peace *could* come true and last through life. This became her reality, not her fantasy.

Chloe and Martha are two of the many men, women, and young people who have experienced what I have known. For more than six decades, I have lived with what I call "joy sensitivity." Peace, joy, and pain relief are genuine in my life. I know how to "refill" them when levels are low. That is what I want to share with you in this book.

- Do you wish there were things you could do to improve your physical health, relationships, and life?

- Are you tired of getting caught in an all too frequent medical or mental health "revolving door" where one diagnosis leads to another and another and another?
- Do you feel helpless to care for your health or have a voice in your medical care?

This book offers straightforward no-cost ways to deal with common, everyday aches and pains.

If you want more options, participation, and influence in your health care and your loved ones' care, this book is for you. Find trustworthy back-to-basics approaches to correct and prevent physical and non-physical pain and problems here.

$$\partial \mathbb{R} \; \partial \mathbb{R} \; \partial \mathbb{R} \; \partial \mathbb{R} \; \partial \mathbb{R}$$

Bonnie's Story

In the early 1980s, I founded *Be Your Best Consulting, LLC*, and *4X4 Healing*, to treat, train, and restore the whole person—not just treat obvious physical symptoms. Here's how it happened.

4X4 Healing — System Unity and Integration

In 1978, I became a Physical Therapist and Lamaze International Childbirth Educator. My specialized training included manual therapy, sport, spine, orthopedic, neurologic, and trauma (childhood and combat) rehabilitation. I saw both male and female patients whose pain and symptoms had no related injury or structural disorder.

James came in with a desire to end his chronic back pain. Treatments helped temporarily, but there seemed to be some underlying unseen cause of his misery. I referred him to a skilled counselor I knew, and we worked together to address James' physical pain and past childhood trauma. His physical pain and body memories ceased when his emotional and spiritual wounds from past abuse healed, along with his physical ailments.

Cheryl had persistent neck pain. She tried many different treatments and medications without relief. Through *4X4 Healing,* her body healed with sensitive, corrective physical therapy. Her neck pain ceased when truth replaced lies she believed about herself, which resulted from painful childhood abuse.

Whether their complaints were vague or specific, I realized these patients had pain and pathology beyond the physical realm. Therefore, I referred them to sensitive, skilled mental health professionals. These counselors effectively diagnosed and treated the closed-head injury, trauma, non-physical causes of pain, cognitive impairment, memory loss, and family or relational dysfunction.

As professionals, we worked to help each patient heal the mind and body. We coordinated both physical therapy treatment and mental health processing to help patients progress more quickly to full healing. When patients dealt with difficult emotional or mental work, I provided comfort, joy, and refreshment, an attentive heart, safe respectful touch, and nurturing care. When counseling was less demanding, and the patient desired new challenges, I pursued more aggressive physical therapy. We focused on manual therapy, structural correction, and integrative training. The goals were to resolve physical pain, structural problems, balance disorders, improve self-care, and build healthy life and relational skills.

This arrangement worked well for years. My insight into the vague causes of these symptoms grew. Eventually, patients who had experienced extreme torture and abuse as young children came to me to heal their physical, functional, and relational difficulties. Working with these patients and their counselors, I confirmed that insightful, broad-scope physical therapy was most effective in achieving long-term comprehensive healing for athletes, accident victims, trauma survivors, and all patients.

As more people sought comprehensive healing, I moved into private practice. There, I scheduled enough time to sensitively address each patient's needs to help them understand the close connection between their physical, emotional, mental, and spiritual wounds. They learned how each one impacts the other. *Be Your Best* grew to include *4X4 Healing*.

What is 4x4 Healing?

4X4 Healing equips you to navigate the challenging terrain of life and health problems through a comprehensive approach of treating and training the whole person. Imagine a 4-wheel-drive vehicle climbing a steep, rocky, narrow trail. All four wheels work independently and in tandem to power up hills and over obstacles to the destination. This imagery perfectly shows the comprehensive healing approach of *4X4 Healing*. Instead of treating symptoms, we identify the root issues and provide tools, treatment, and training which promote lasting improvement.

4x4 Components

- **Body**. In addition to manifesting visible injury or dysfunction, your body expresses your heart, mind, and spirit's unseen pain.
- **Mind**. Distorted thinking alters your perspectives, decisions, relationships, self-care, and stress levels—all these impact your body.
- **Emotion**. The pain in your body affects how you feel—just as your emotional pain and injuries affect your physical structure.
- **Spirit**. Your spirit is the eternal part of you. Your beliefs and values, along with the presence of spiritually-generated joy, peace, and contentment in your life and relationships (or lack thereof), have a profound effect on your physical condition.

It is important to consider and tend to all four areas in treating the symptoms and the causes of pain and problems.

Through the healing process, we incorporate four additional elements:

- **Educate.** Learn the causes and possible corrections of your pain and problems (not just symptoms) and why the healing process is trustworthy.
- **Explore.** Assess and identify areas that require healing and care to determine the direction for your healing journey (with support and encouragement from a trained, caring, 4x4 Healing coach).
- **Equip.** Practice skills that increase peace, joy, rest, freedom, and wholeness in life developed with your coach's support and guidance.
- **Empower**. Practice and establish new healthy perspectives, choices, and self-care in daily life for vibrant health and lasting improvement.

It takes determination and commitment to decide you will not allow yourself to *settle* into needless limitations. Gather your courage to heal deep wounds and take each step of your healing journey toward freedom and function—it is so worth the effort to change your life for the best! We will discuss more fully, in the following sections, how the body remembers and reflects the condition of your mind, emotions, and spirit. Whether you know it or not, what you believe is what you live.

Physical Therapy = Patient Teacher

Knowledgeable physical therapists equip you to improve physical function and life skills, whether your pain and problems result from injury, wear and tear, or deeply-harbored hurts. Again, whether damage occurs to the mind, heart, spirit, or body, all systems are impacted. Comprehensive physical therapy treatment and retraining connect the whole person experientially (the body with its mental, emotional, and spiritual components). Purely structural problems also resolve faster and more thoroughly in a combined physical-mental-emotional-spiritual treatment approach.

Survivors of trauma often must learn how to stop habitual protective hypervigilance (tension, guarding, and feeling unsafe in non-threatening situations) in daily life. Deep internal hurts (especially those suffered at an early age) can trigger extreme emotional reactions, headaches, digestive discomfort, balance loss, recurring negative relational cycles, and self-limiting lies. These wounds generate unrealistic fear-based messages which destroy coping, hope, joy, imagination, creativity, and initiative.

Through *4x4 Healing*, patients and counselors consistently report faster progress. Patients who have been told "It's all in your mind," "Learn to live with it," or "There's nothing we can do" often feel hopeless and helpless. Then they wonder whether or not they might be losing their minds. By simultaneously addressing the deep non-physical contributors and the physical problems, strange symptoms and nebulous, multiple diagnoses resolve. In every case, motivated patients experience benefits and improvement.

ﻌ ﻌ ﻌ ﻌ ﻌ

Do you feel frustrated because your treatment plan seems to lead from one problem to another?

Do your prescribed medications and treatments address immediate symptoms without correcting root causes?

Over the more than forty years that I have served as a physical therapist, our health care system has moved from treating the whole person to treating specific areas and seeming to trust technology more than listening to the patient.

My heart is to educate and equip you with back-to-basics knowledge you need to become aware of preventable problems and take charge of your health care.

Though often tiring, this work energizes me as I see people committed to be their best and settling for nothing less. I love the amazing transformation that occurs when a person wants to be whole, healed, and free. There are joys and benefits beyond imagination when a person chooses to journey with a skilled coach and travel a path to restore the heart, mind, spirit, and body. That is what *4X4 Healing* and this book address.

These vital issues require our attention, both in the physical therapy profession and in medical and mental health specialties. It's imperative to bridge the gap between the physical and non-physical aspects of care.

This guide *offers options for your consideration and equips you* to join the conversation and participate in your health care proactively. It is not intended to replace medical care or critical individual evaluation, diagnosis, and treatment. However, it does offer insights, options, and proven approaches for you to explore.

There are good reasons for the body to act and react as it does.

Nancy, my friend, and patient who granted permission to use her name, intends to read this book at least once each year to remember what she learned and improve her ability to apply the healthful hints presented there.

The stories in this book represent a variety of people with similar symptoms. Real names are used only with permission.

ৡৈ ৡৈ ৡৈ ৡৈ ৡৈ

Talk to professionals who know you, share your values, and understand your conditions. Teamwork depends on honest, open discussion. Actively participate with your providers and your support community to achieve your desired goals. As you read this information, remember that I am speaking to those who want change, are willing to investigate healing potential, and who can make changes. For people who are limited by insurmountable disabilities, I applaud and rejoice your courage not to settle and your effort to be your best. These are concepts for your consideration. I encourage you to seek professional individual evaluation and guidance, especially if you are not improving.

Additionally, this information does not mean to judge or offend in any way. You have choices. It is important to know truthful realistic alternatives available so that you can make the best decisions. You are respected and valued as a human being. I want to offer options with the hope that you will *be your best*!

Navigating This Book

Each Part has four sections.

1. **Do You Know?** A clear introduction to and explanation of the topic.
2. **Food for Thought**. Practical discussion of the topic.
3. **Let's Do This**! Personal application and activities related to the topic.
4. **Train to Maintain**. Ways to incorporate the principles into your lifestyle and key points to remember.

Watch for this image:

 It's your sign to look for additional information in the Appendices or on my website.

PART ONE
THE BASICS

"You can't fail if you don't quit. You can't succeed if you don't start."

Michael Hyatt

Photo by Jon Tyson on Unsplash

SECTION 1
DO YOU KNOW?

CHAPTER 1

Hope in a Hurting World: You Are Not Alone

My heart aches when I encounter people who have recurring pain or doubt whether they can improve physical problems. Men and women of all ages cry out to function more freely and stop their pain.

A little education goes a long way.

Often, simple instructions work to relieve pain, remedy physical problems, improve relationships, manage stress, and find deep internal peace. For example:

- Several men working in construction found immediate relief through ergonomic training that improved their framing, drywall, and roofing jobs. Others found that postural instruction, proper use of ice, and (where appropriate) industrial back support for strenuous activity resolved their pain. All acknowledged "a little education goes a long way." Each man benefited from an individualized Independent Home Program (IHP) to improve back health and prevent pain or injury.
- An elderly lady struggled to breathe and complained of acid reflux. One medication blossomed into many, raising her prescription costs with no end in sight. Instead of accepting the temporary symptom relief, she looked for a cure. When she came in for physical therapy, she learned she habitually slouched while sitting

and standing. She also discovered her slouching compromised her breathing and digestive functions. When she corrected her posture, her comfort and breathing improved immediately. As she strengthened her back and maintained a good stance, her reflux decreased, and with her physician's guidance, she got off all medications. Correcting her posture, learning to relax, preventing worry that causes more gastric acid, and sipping water through the day resolved her problems.

- Pregnant women in their third trimester can also experience reflux symptoms. In addition to the previous methods, these women can ease the reflux associated with pregnancy by raising their left arm overhead, giving more space to internal organs.

This book offers straightforward, no-cost ways to deal with common, everyday aches and pains. Yes, symptoms come from a vast array of contributors, and each person has a unique history needing individualized care. No, you won't find a quick-fix recipe that fits everyone's needs or a cure-all for your specific condition. What you will find are proven initial and basic approaches that help in most cases or might set you on a productive pathway to lasting improvement. So, whether you are injured, over-worked, over-stressed, stuck in a rut, a survivor of abuse or trauma, suffering from athletic injuries, struggling with unhealthy boundaries, or facing the effects of age, here are consistent successes experienced in over forty years of being a physical therapist.

Through the years, I worked with many counselors. We know there is a strong connection between physical problems and deep, internal, non-physical pain. Emotional, mental, and spiritual wounds can be expressed physically just as physical attack and injury can be expressed emotionally, mentally, and spiritually.

ॐ ॐ ॐ ॐ ॐ

Dan walked into my office slowly, carefully. With every step, his face grimaced in pain. His body shifted to one side. He walked gingerly with a limp. He preferred to stand because he experienced severe leg pain after sitting. Exhaustion grew from lack of sleep. Over the last few months, tension rose in Dan's family due to his inability to work, his relentless pain, and his short temper. His family felt distressed, not knowing how to help him.

Dan had tried several treatment approaches. Though the problems seemed to improve, the benefits were always temporary. He still looked for help to correct the cause of his pain so he could drive, get back to work, and sleep at night. Tired of being tired, Dan was ready to participate fully in his healing journey.

Dan learned the cumulative causes of his pain and how to correct and prevent them. He and his family learned about stress management and relational support. Also, Dan consistently performed his Independent Home Program (IHP) as instructed. Not only was this man's pain and growing numbness eliminated, but he was also able to return to work in a few short weeks. Now Dan knew what he could do to prevent the problems from recurring. His family provided support and helped him to remember the key points of his self-care and IHP. Through the four months of his training and treatment, he and his family gained insights and skills that equipped them to prevent and manage both pain and injury for life.

❧ ❧ ❧ ❧ ❧

Over the last forty to fifty years, research has consistently indicated that 80-90% of people will suffer back pain in their lives. In 2009, a study showed Americans who experience low back pain lose more than $100 billion annually due to lost wages, reduced productivity, and treatment costs.[1]

Medical care can cascade into multiple diagnoses, accumulating treatment costs, a growing list of medications, and more. If you have a history of abuse or trauma, you may have several diagnoses that "haunt" you but are never cured. By dealing with the physical ailments concurrently with the deep, invisible wounds of the heart, mind, and spirit, you experience unimagined healing that lasts.

There are many kinds and causes of suffering. Physical problems are visible but may not be the most debilitating or torturous. Statistically, one in four girls and one in six boys experience sexual abuse before age 18 (though many cases go unreported). Child abuse, sexual abuse, and domestic violence throughout the world are horrific and heartbreaking. America is not immune. The National Association of Adult Survivors of Child Abuse website reports that over 42 million Americans experience sexual abuse. Conservatively, 20%-25% of America's youth currently or will experience sexual abuse. These sobering statistics do not include reported and unreported domestic violence, emotional abuse, or child and elder neglect cases.[2, 3]

Each year, about 1.5 million women and close to 835,000 men are raped or physically assaulted by someone close to them. Approximately two out of every three women who report rape, assault, and stalking are repeatedly abused. Americans spend over $5.8 billion every year toward health care for rape, physical assault, and stalking victims.[4] There is so much pain in this world—it is overwhelming.

As my patients share their hearts and hurts, I fight hard to keep my focus on the *hope* and healing potential. It would be easy to become trapped by past pain or fall into paralyzing depression at the horrors perpetrated against these courageous precious people.

Maybe you came from a difficult, painful childhood or lived through combat trauma. My heart aches with yours. I desire to encourage you and share approaches to help you experience healing, improvement, and peace. Comprehensive healing results in improvement. Coming from deep pain and darkness into freedom and light takes courage and time, but the resulting joy, peace, and full function far outweigh the effort.

Survivors of childhood trauma often seek help initially for physical and balance problems. Reasonably, we start with managing the physical pain and difficulties—remembering that the body, mind, emotions, and spirit are intimately interconnected.

CHAPTER 2

Signs of Deep Wounds: Change Your Hurts to Healing

Your body expresses physical injury. However, your body may also express deep non-physical hurts through physical symptoms. If you ignore invisible internal wounds, your physical problems persist. Our physical, mental, emotional, and spiritual parts are intricately interdependent and intertwined. One area affects the others.

Is life pain-free? No, of course not. But there are things we can do to heal past wounds and deal with discomfort as they arise. Unresolved effects of trauma—ranging from mild to severe—interfere with normal function.

Everyone experiences fleeting episodes of some symptoms listed below, but typically, these symptoms will not persist, interfere with function, or worsen over time. Some symptoms may be present due to a lack of training or self-discipline. If these symptoms do continue in your life, don't give up. When you address the sources of problems, remarkable, consistent, and lasting improvements result.

In the following list, check any of the symptoms you experience. Add any others that you want to discuss with your health care providers—and keep reading! This book's information may take care of the problem or guide you and your providers to more effective approaches.

Common, persistent signs and symptoms resulting from trauma may include:

- ❑ Loss of memory, periods of blackout, or gaps in time
- ❑ Secrecy, guilt, shame, fear, constant worry
- ❑ Cloudy or confused mental functioning
- ❑ Poor self-esteem
- ❑ Feeling you have no voice, have no value, or don't exist
- ❑ Feeling unsafe much of the time
- ❑ Involvement in relationships which create, maintain, or tolerate unhealthy boundaries
- ❑ Distrust of God and people
- ❑ Fragmented lifestyle (procrastination, disorganized, hard to keep promises or schedule, etc.)
- ❑ Just "surviving or existing" approach to life—unaware of options, "I don't deserve good things"
- ❑ Self-persecution
- ❑ Blaming others—avoiding personal responsibility for your choices, words, actions
- ❑ Victim mentality
- ❑ Destructive lifestyle, self-mutilation (cutting, burning, dangerous environments, and activities, etc.)
- ❑ Nightmares, flashbacks, triggers, PTSD
- ❑ Inappropriate threat reactions without actual danger (triggers)
- ❑ Exaggerated emotional responses: anger, personal offense, defensiveness, etc.
- ❑ Depression, hopelessness
- ❑ Physical pain and symptoms such as
  - o Recurring headaches
  - o Digestive/GI problems/IBS
  - o Chronic Fatigue
  - o Fibromyalgia
  - o Chronic Pain Syndrome
  - o Rashes and skin eruptions
  - o Multiple, vague, and on-going diagnoses without resolution
  - o Stress-related diseases
- ❑ Insomnia and sleep difficulties
- ❑ Eating disorders

Harbored hurts (which can cause symptoms listed previously) affect how you see your life, your identity, your relationships, and the world. They also determine how you handle stress.

How Do You Manage Stress?

While people commonly consider stress as harmful, stress has a purpose. It will either break you down or build you up. To understand the positive or negative impact of stress, it is crucial to:

1. **Define your stress**—How do you perceive stress? Its definition varies with time. Sometimes your stress is physical, sometimes mental, emotional, or spiritual. Is your stress due to concerns about health or finances? Do you feel anxiety about your marriage, children, or other personal relationships? Are you constantly inconvenienced and frustrated because of slow-moving traffic, delayed plans, or children needing attention?
2. **Identify what can or cannot be changed**—What can alleviate your stress? Can you ask another person for help or to make a change? Can you release factors that you cannot change to God?
3. **Discover its benefits**—What can you learn from the stress you feel? How can this stress help you become stronger, more resilient, or delegate responsibility?
4. **Remember tough times that you have survived with God's help**—Write down past crises and what brought you through. Review these victories when you feel fearful, depressed, or overwhelmed.

Managing stress increases your ability to tolerate more demanding situations successfully. We become physically stronger when we repeatedly handle uncomfortable demands well. This principle especially applies to relationship skills and growth. Managing relationship challenges well helps us to recognize, build, and practice better communication to resolve conflict and improve outcomes.

When a real or perceived situation overwhelms you, adrenaline releases into your system, which causes a "flight-fight-freeze" response. This response to life-threatening conditions saves you. But the constant release of adrenaline or cortisol is detrimental physically, emotionally, and mentally. It results in a prolonged state of hypervigilance. This condition of exaggerated muscle guarding, defensive readiness, and perceived threat raises your blood pressure and heart rate, interferes with sleep and daily function, and increases fatigue. Replace exaggerated threat reactions and beliefs with appropriate perceptions and responses.

Survivors of childhood abuse may not be aware of their hypervigilant condition until healing begins. The investment of time required for treatment and practice is priceless for learning appropriate responses and building healthy habits. Unless there is real danger present, hypervigilance is exhausting and unhealthy.

Both physical and non-physical pain and symptom contributors must be recognized and treated for lasting restoration and full function to become healthy.

CHAPTER 3

Three Interactive Elements: Fear, Pain, and Tension

Think about when you feel fear, struggle to pay your bills, or have an emotional disagreement with a loved one. Where do you feel the tension? Most people have a specific area of their body that tenses first. For my husband, it is an area in his back where he sustained a motorcycle injury as a young man. As for me, my shoulders tense first. Physical therapy involves considerable upper-body work, and so those muscles react first to surprise, fear, or distress.

Fear, pain, and tension are natural reactions to an unknown, unexpected, intense sensation or fright. This Fear-Pain-Tension Cycle can start with any of the three elements. It is clearly seen during childbirth. As a physical therapist and childbirth educator, I worked extensively with prenatal, laboring, and postpartum women. I successfully taught prenatal and postpartum patients how to manage pregnancy's common discomforts, and I served as a doula—coaching couples during labor and delivery.

Imagine a woman who is pregnant for the first time, now in labor. Maybe you have been the laboring woman or have attended a woman in labor. When the mother has been trained for labor and has loving, trained support present, the practical tools they learned minimize childbirth stress and pain.

If this first-time mother is alone during her labor and has not been trained to handle the demands of her unique labor experience, she naturally falls into a Fear-Pain-Tension Cycle.

The less you understand about the cause, scope, or purpose of your discomfort and the less prepared you are for the sensations, the greater the negative impact of your pain, fear, and tension.

Pain, anxiety, and fear cause increased muscle tension, which uses more oxygen. Tight, over-worked muscles also hinder circulation, which increases pain. Breathing is often shallow or stops altogether during pain or fear experiences. Decreased oxygen increases pain—which in turn feeds the fear and tension.

The Fear-Pain-Tension Cycle

You see how this cycle can build quickly and lead to panic, intense pain, and tetany (sustained muscle spasm). Prolonged muscle contraction cuts circulation and oxygen to working muscles, causing increased pain. Muscle tension compresses nerves, leading to tingling, numbness, more pain, and loss of function—all of which can be scary. That is how the cycle feeds itself and grows. Usually, you react in fear when you experience pain that surprises you with its occurrence or intensity. Fright can be multifaceted.

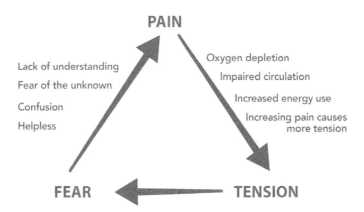

Anxiety in feeling no control can build through questions we ask ourselves, for example:

- How long will this pain last?
- How great will this growing pain become?
- What is happening to my body?
- What is happening to the baby?

If the mother is unprepared, apprehensive, and reactively tenses during the normal labor process, medical staff curbs the Fear-Pain-Tension Cycle through encouragement and medication.

The Fear-Pain-Tension-Cycle is the default human reaction to any real or perceived threat, discomfort, or worry. However, education, training, and practice minimize progressive, inappropriate reactions and detrimental effects. This cycle is active in any person who feels alone, scared, or unsafe. When no danger is present, the Fear-Pain-Tension Cycle can accelerate inappropriately and cause harmful reactions. Learn to control this cycle and usefully redirect energy to avoid adverse physical, mental, emotional, and spiritual repercussions.

If the problem or pain returns, the cause of the problem has not been corrected.

Check out the Appendix:
Active Relaxation

CHAPTER 4
Pain — Good or Bad?: Listen To Your Body

Discomfort can mean many different things. When pain is quantified medically, we use a 10-point scale, where "0" indicates that you are not aware of any abnormal sensations and "10" is torturous—an emergency room visit.

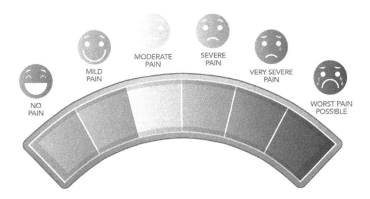

PAIN ASSESSMENT TOOL

When people talk about their hurts, they can mean many things:

- Soreness from a long day on the job
- An athletic workout
- Deep bone ache

- Gut distress after surgery
- A paper cut
- A migraine that lasts for days
- A mild bump on the head
- A deep bruise from a fall
- A tender bottom from sitting too long
- Other definitions

When you are fighting to save your life, or another's life, you may hardly notice the sensations because your objective and focus are so powerful during the painful event. How a person views the cause of his or her suffering and believes about the hurt they experience dramatically influences the level of misery perceived.

Many patients who come for physical therapy report real torment when no physical or medical cause can be identified. However, the intensity, frequency, and duration of symptoms are lower when there is a sense of hope in what they believe about their complaints. Chronic symptoms persist when a person believes:

- He or she has no control over the pain, the cause, or their condition
- The pain is from some unidentifiable source
- Someone else caused the problem
- The pain or illness cannot be changed, improved, or resolved
- I am receiving attention or other benefit from my pain or problem

Without exploring and addressing these deep beliefs, you quickly fall into feeling hopeless, helpless, and controlled by outside forces. On the other hand, research shows if a person believes his or her pain is temporary, has a noble purpose, can be managed, or improved, the affliction is much less debilitating. So, suffering is subjective, with a broad scope of personal interpretation.

Good vs. Bad Pain

You can carry the phrase "no pain, no gain" too far. "Pain" can be suitable discomfort in attaining a desirable healthy goal or a danger warning that tissues are damaged. So, there is such a thing as *good pain*. And there is *bad pain*, so let's look at each.

We will define *bad* pain as an overpowering sensation that makes you want to pull away, run away, tense, or fight. I cannot think of a controllable situation where bad pain has a positive purpose. Beyond the blessing of anesthetics and pain medications, you can choose medical procedures or training challenges that may be painful but focus on the prize beyond the pain to get through it.

Maybe you cannot actively relax during the treatment because the intensity is overwhelming. Do you remember the Pain-Tension-Fear cycle? The cycle starts with any of the three components. If your breathing becomes shallow or stops and the fear builds, you tense and want to run away. Bad pain (sensation you cannot handle) may compromise the procedure's purpose and desired result. It is beneficial to learn more than one method to prevent or transform bad pain.

Good pain is discomfort that indicates activity in the right direction—working in the right area to resolve the problem. You can intentionally relax during this discomfort with a purpose. It is manageable—maybe it "hurts so good." You recognize the benefits beyond the pain. We call this work (like training for a marathon, walking stairs for alignment and strength, or "labor" to deliver a baby).

Discomfort from healthy working is controllable. The pain involved in the necessary treatment or the soreness you feel from getting stronger resolves. Manageable stress is needed to grow and build strength, endurance, and resiliency. We live in "move it or lose it" bodies. You experience persistent and increasing (bad) pain from poor work-rest balance, over-exerting, being too sedentary, or falling into poor alignment.

Through over forty years of physical therapy practice, I have never seen a reason to cause *bad pain* in treatment. Beneficial and lasting results come from the hurt-so-good *(good pain)* or *work* without over-stressing the tissues. One of my standards in physical therapy is to *ask, don't force.* I ask for more range, more repetitions, better alignment, but the strengthening, stretching, or treatment sensations are manageable.

When I had my knees replaced, my job was to ask for more motion, more strength *continually.* I didn't cause myself agony. Throughout the day, I felt manageable discomfort of gently, *consistently* requesting a bit more than my preferred limitations. Within six months, my legs felt like part of me again. I could run and jump, which had been increasingly difficult and finally impossible over the 44 years since I had torn them up in gymnastics at age 16.

A Pain Management Tool: Breathe-Melt-Wiggle (B-M-W)

What do you recall about the Flight-Fight-Freeze survival response? Do you remember the associated adrenaline release, increased heart rate, defensive readiness, and increased muscle tension? Often, people who endured childhood abuse or combat trauma overreact in defensive ways when normal, safe, daily events trigger protective reactions. These defensive reflexes automatically fuel the Fear-Pain-Tension Cycle. These reactions are especially powerful when ingrained past sensitivity feeds the perceived fear. For instance, a soldier reacts to a balloon popping just as he did to an IED explosion. A woman who survived rape panics when someone walks behind her or a friend rushes to give her a friendly hug.

One of the tools I use to stop and appropriately retrain inappropriate or adverse physical reactions is B-M-W (Breathe-Melt-Wiggle). It's easy to remember because it's the name of a car. But in this case, it's not a car—it's a lifestyle.

When you B-M-W, you build a habit of preventing fear and panic reactions. No more freezing like a deer in the headlights and falling into the Fear-Pain-Tension Cycle. This tool allows your brain to calm itself, override immediate emotional impulses, and accurately evaluate the situation. It's like counting to ten before you react with strong emotions. Your brain responds maturely to assess your options and provide perspective. You maintain control of yourself instead of letting knee-jerk emotional reactions and outside forces control you.

When no actual danger is present, take time to practice. Each B-M-W action has benefits:

B = *Breathe* **a slow deep breath evenly, in and out.** Take a full gradual inhale followed by an equal exhale to oxygenate your brain and body effectively. Slow, in-and-out breathing allows clear thinking for escape and evasion when danger is present. Proper oxygenation also allows your mind to analyze a situation accurately when reactionary habits and emotions are strong, and there is no threat.

M = *Melt* **like butter.** Turn off all unnecessary muscle tension from the top of your head to the tips of your toes. Just as turning off all appliances from the attic to the basement saves energy in your home, *melting* conserves energy and increases awareness of where you are holding tension.

W = *Wiggle.* It's hard to be tense when you are doing the hula, so keep dancing! Wiggle after you have been still for a while to *wake up* your joints, muscles, and circulation. Wiggling helps relieve joint stiffness, improve muscle function and balance, and engage your brain before getting out of bed, after prolonged sitting, or any static position. Wiggling improves your motor responses. It helps you wake up at night and gets your brain working to prevent tripping and falling.

Check out the B-M-W videos, eBook, and more at my website: 4x4Healing.com

B-M-W is a simple habit to develop for dealing with stress or discomfort—emotional or physical.

For improved circulation and lower leg health, practice what I call *happy feet* to prevent tired, sore feet. First, lift your toes and then your heels, move your ankles in all directions, wiggle your toes. Happy feet and weight-shifting while standing also decreases lower leg and foot swelling or tingling, increases circulation, and prevents varicose veins. Do this while you are sitting—especially on airplanes, long car rides, or at work. Do the hula or shift your weight while standing in one place when on the phone, at work, in a grocery store line, cooking, etc. Whatever you do, don't plant those feet—keep 'em moving!

CHAPTER 5

We All Need Advocacy: Help Yourself and Loved Ones

Stop and Start

Pain is personal. Only you can determine what sensation and intensity you can tolerate, so you must use your voice and advocate for yourself. Whether you are in a hospital or clinic, with a doctor, dentist, physical therapist, nurse, massage therapist, personal trainer, or any health care provider, you must be safe and respected. Ask a trusted loved one or friend to advocate on your behalf when needed.

You have the right to say, "Stop." This goes for any new, unknown, or uncomfortable situation. Even if you don't know what makes you feel confused or uneasy, you can and should say, "Stop." Saying "Stop" is an excellent practice for you and helps your provider know your needs.

When you go for health care, do you feel you have control? Health care providers are there for you, the patient—you are not there for the provider. Be bold respectfully. Tell your provider that you may want to say "Stop" to ask questions. Practice B-M-W, relax actively, and prepare to respond to whatever will happen next. Your provider can help you respond to the procedure

Participating in your care increases the quality of your care.

in the best way. Encourage your providers to partner with you in your care. Your providers pay more attention to you when they know you care about what is happening and actively participate.

Your ability to say, "Stop" and "Start" makes your care most satisfying for all involved. I make it a habit to practice both "Stop" and "Start" with my patients. Those activities are essential to express your voice, increase your self-awareness, and feel safe and respected. Practicing these skills helps you grow in confidence that you *are* heard and honored (which can be a new experience for trauma survivors). Exercising your voice and your choice is even more critical when you have never asserted yourself in this way. Many healing and system-unifying effects result from saying "Stop" and "Start" during your care. We'll discuss this subject in greater detail in the Mind chapter of this book.

Identify an Advocate

Advocacy is a fundamental principle in health care. When you act as your health care advocate, you are proactive. You ask people for recommendations. You let providers know your needs and discomforts because you are self-aware and able to communicate your condition. You let providers know your medications and allergies. You monitor your medications and the quality of your care.

When you cannot let providers know your needs or monitor your care, you need a prepared, trustworthy, caring health care advocate. This person becomes your quality control and voice when you are too sick or incapacitated to look after your own needs.

When you go to receive medical care, have the following items handy. Find a trustworthy, caring friend or family member to advocate for you when you are unable. Make sure your advocate has this information as well:

1. **Your wishes and goals for medical care.** Write down your feelings, desires, and goals for your medical care and give a copy to your advocate before it is too late—when

you cannot communicate your wishes. Be sure the person you choose as an advocate will recognize and honor your preferences and goals during treatment.

2. **Your written medical history, updated medication list, and Medical Power of Attorney.** Only one Advocate can make medical choices if you are unable. Family and friends can counsel you and work with the medical staff as long as you can make your own decisions. But, if a legal authorization is needed and you cannot communicate your choices, your Medical Power of Attorney is worthless if you have designated more than one decision-maker. Too often, the desires of the well-meaning family or friends conflict. The medical staff must honor the patient's goals and wishes. Therefore, it is essential to have your Medical Power of Attorney designated to one person and signed before needed.

3. **Your questions about the intended medical care.** Ideally, your advocate will ask questions on your behalf, inform you about your options, and make decisions according to your wishes.

4. **Your desired care plan during and after the medical care.** Your advocate lets the staff know your comfort needs while in the hospital or during treatment, and helps you remember details about your home-care responsibilities. Your advocate is a resource of strength and support when you need assistance.

Think about the last time you visited or were a patient in a hospital. The staff is busy and not able to identify all patient needs immediately. Your advocate is attentive to your comfort by letting staff know you need a blanket, more water, or assistance to get to the bathroom, etc. An advocate protects your privacy by closing doors or keeping you covered. The very presence of an interested caring person during your treatment promotes positive quality control and impacts your recovery's success.

Advocacy is valuable in any care situation. Your advocate supports you, writes down important information, and helps prevent misunderstandings between you and your provider. The presence of a third party during your care also decreases the risk of frivolous lawsuits.

When should you seek help?

Don't be shy. Ask for help when you want it and when it is best for you. Contact a medical, dental, or mental health provider to discuss your situation or when you need more information. Even if you don't know why you want professional help, go when you feel the need.

Use self-care remedies initially and appropriately when you feel under the weather, like rest, prayer, gentle heat, effective ice, massage, chicken soup, vitamin C, and non-prescription pain medicine. If your condition does not improve within three to five days or increases in intensity, frequency, or duration, get a professional evaluation. Remember, the goal is safety first!

SECTION 2
FOOD FOR THOUGHT

CHAPTER 6

Have A Voice in Your Care: You Are Part of The Team

Shopping for the best expertise and quality to meet your health care needs is undoubtedly essential, no matter what service or product you seek. Don't be afraid to ask questions. Everyone working with you *must* have a plan and reason for what they do. The most effective treatment involves your active teamwork with your provider. You need to understand the treatment plan and the procedures that will move you toward your goals. You don't need extensive knowledge of medicine or the provider's specialty. Mainly, asking Who-What-When-Where-Why-How will give you valuable information and generate more questions.

For example, Doug went to the doctor for an illness. He received antibiotics to handle the disease. However, because of the lab results, he also was diagnosed with diabetes. His physician prescribed three appropriate medications for the diabetes diagnosis.

Doug asked about the pros and cons of each medication. Then, he asked, "What would happen if I don't take the medications? Are there other options for changing future lab results?" The doctor suggested he could take only one medication, or he could exercise, lose some weight, and recheck his blood work in three months.

Doug chose to refuse all medicines, deciding to exercise and lose weight. The result was fantastic. He exercised moderately without changing his diet or sacrificing any of the foods he enjoyed. He just decreased the size of his meals and took a walk at least three times per week. In three months, he lost 20 pounds, and his lab work indicated he was pre-diabetic. His six-month check confirmed his A1C continued to drop without medication.

Additionally, he felt better and had more energy. Maintaining his lower weight, he had low diabetic markers and no symptoms of diabetes. Doug would *never have known there was a non-medication option* for improvement if he had not asked. If you want more information, be bold. Be proactive and *ask* if there are other possibilities—in the diagnosis and treatment!

Health Care Shopping

We live in a time of incredible medical advances and knowledge. As with every service and product, carefully consider the options, benefits, and risks before purchasing. Our society and medical community have progressively moved toward reliance on technology over a relationship, with a strong desire in both patient and provider for instant gratification—the quick fix. These trends lead to diagnostic labels without cure, treatments or surgery without improvement, and misdiagnoses without considering past trauma and stress reactions. To prevent these tendencies, remember that medical professionals are there to serve you. You have the right and personal responsibility to understand:

- The cause(s) of your pain and problems
- Your treatment options
- Benefits and risks of the planned treatments and procedures
- Other available options

You have the right to understand all test results, your provider's interpretation, and plan of care. Review the possible adverse outcomes, as well as the desired positive results. Request an explanation of the treatment plan, the progression, and your responsibility in language you clearly understand. Ask how they reached their conclusions. As you receive answers, ask more questions as they come to mind.

Here are some questions to ask as you communicate with your provider:

- Would you please show me how you came to your conclusions? I want to see the X-rays, CT, MRI, or other test results. Please describe what is wrong and what normal looks like.
- What else could cause my pain and symptoms?
- Could stress or past trauma cause these symptoms? Please explain.
- Please clarify the known and possible physical and non-physical causes of my pain and problem.
- Please share your plan of care and explain the process and my responsibilities.

Inquiry and questions like these help you consider holistic approaches and non-invasive possibilities before accepting invasive procedures like surgery.

Remember that physical pain and problems can develop from non-physical wounds. Consider how deep mental, emotional, spiritual wounds and lies affect your health and life. This reflection can reveal paths to comprehensive healing that purely medical approaches cannot provide.

ॐ ॐ ॐ ॐ ॐ

Do you feel safe and in control when you are in a new situation? How do you keep fear, panic, and negative reactions from controlling you in new or unknown situations? Do you remember the handy tool B-M-W? It's easy to remember—it's a car brand. Counting to ten may cause you to hesitate or settle your mind, but it does not stop the physical stress reactions. B-M-W does it all. Think through the process:

B = Breathe: Breathe equally—slowly and deeply, in and out.

M = Melt: Melt like butter, turning off all unnecessary muscle tension from head to toe.

W = Wiggle: Wiggle—move trunk and extremities. "Dancing" makes it hard to tense up. After being still for a while, wiggle to "wake up" your joints, muscles, circulation, and mind.

Let's practice. Have you been sitting for a while? It's time to B-M-W. Sit up straight to give your lungs room to work and prevent back pain:

First, "B": *Breathe* slowly and evenly, in and out. As you breathe deeply and slowly, begin to relax.

Second, "M": *Melt* like butter. From the top of your head to the tip of your toes, tighten and then completely relax muscles in your scalp, head, neck, shoulders, upper back, arms/hands, mid-back, and abdomen. If you want to comfort your abdomen, try rubbing your tummy tenderly in a circle, up on the right side and down on the left side, working from the outer edges, moving closer to your navel with each slow circle. If massaging your abdomen makes you feel tense or uncomfortable, stop. Continue *melting*—your low back, pelvis, legs, and feet. Continue this exercise of tightening and fully letting go from head to toes and toes to head as you melt deeper into the chair or mattress with each slow exhale. Stay there and *feel* your body supported as you breathe slowly and sink deeper into the support.

Third, "W": *Wiggle* your feet and hands leisurely. Gently rock your hips back and forth. Tuck your chin slightly back toward your neck, then make tiny "yes" nods and "no" rotations.

Can you think of a time that **B-M-W** would have decreased your fear or tension? Practice through the day—***Every time*** you see the color **red** (stop signs, stop lights, clothes, items on your desk, etc.), practice B-M-W!

SECTION 3
LET'S DO THIS!

CHAPTER 7

A Place to Start: How Sturdy Is Your Foundation?

Now that we've covered some health care basics, you may be saying, "Good information, but where do I start?" The best place to begin is with a sturdy foundation.

The Foundation

Excellent posture establishes your solid, durable physical foundation. Each person needs postural correction regardless of your gender, weight, fitness level, age, height, body composition, or build. It makes no sense to correct structural problems if your alignment is faulty—you trade one trouble for another. Let's do it right the first time to avoid a revolving door of cascading problems and "do-overs."

Proper posture centers joint movement, balancing the length and strength of the muscles and soft tissues around joints. It allows for effective tracking (bone-on-bone alignment) through the movement. It also prevents irritation and degenerative changes. Wolff's law states: bones will adapt to the forces placed upon them.[5]

The combination of proper alignment and posture strengthens bones, joints, and supportive tissues. As the illustration shows, your ear should be over the point of your shoulder, shoulder over hip joint, hip joint over the knee, with the line continuing to your foot a bit forward of the ankle joint.

ക്ഷ ക്ഷ ക്ഷ ക്ഷ ക്ഷ

Why is it important to practice and build good postural habits? As stated earlier, proper posture promotes optimal skeletal growth and joint function. Sitting and standing erect allows room for the best breathing volume (vital capacity), digestion, and internal organ function. Postural alignment builds soft tissue and muscle length and strength balance, prevents structural and mechanical pain, and allows full function. The balance of tissue length and strength around each joint means the joint remains centralized during the full range of motion.

When some muscles, tendons, and other soft tissues are too tight, too powerful, too loose, or weak (out of balance), the joint becomes off-center. Spinal malalignment increases joint, disc, and tissue stress, which results in spinal degeneration, arthritis, and nerve compression. Muscle length and strength imbalance around the kneecap causes chondromalacia (painful or "crunchy," noisy kneecap function) and possible patellar (kneecap) dislocation. With a strong core (muscles and tissues close to the spine in proper balance), your arms and legs work most effectively.

Picture a large construction crane, backhoe, or excavator with a long, sturdy working arm to lift, dig, or reposition heavy objects. How effective would it be without a

substantial anchor or counterweight foundation on which to move? That working arm would be useless, unable to function, and would fall to the ground!

Too many human bodies consist of powerful arms and legs connected by "mush." Poor posture decreases our core strength and stability. Sedentary lifestyles contribute to weak trunk muscles. Both of those trends contribute to functional limitations along with nerve, joint, and muscle pain.

Check out the Appendix:
Key Concepts for Injury Prevention

Beyond Yourself

The final and most important fundamental element of essential good health in body, mind, heart (emotions), and spirit is knowing and following our Creator. When you buy a new car, it is important to read the instructions for care and operation. It's the same for you and me. We only meet our joy and functional potential when we live as our Creator intends. I'm not talking about a religion of man-made "shoulds" and rules. I'm talking about a relationship of trust beyond human understanding with The One who designed and made you. This relationship generates a desire to please and honor our Creator's instructions and identity—just like a child feels about a good parent. Knowing and trusting the True Creator gives joy, strength, peace, and resilience beyond yourself to get through tough times. If you have questions about how and why I know this, please reach out to me!

SECTION 4
TRAIN TO MAINTAIN

CHAPTER 8

Take Your First Step: What Are You Waiting For?

You are a dynamic being—you don't remain the same over time. Human beings either actively improve or passively regress. To break a bad habit, you must replace it with a good one. Though you may not feel any benefit when you start, having clear written reminders of why you want to change your bad habit or behavior makes all the difference. If you don't *value* the new practice more highly than the old one, you won't change.

Studies show it takes about 5,000 repetitions for muscle memory and function to change. But the good news is you don't have to do those corrections all at once. The key is *not to slip back into old, bad habits* and positions.

Think of it like pouring concrete. You set the molds and pour the concrete. The molds support the concrete until the concrete is set and strong enough to hold its shape. If you remove the molds

You either actively improve or passively regress.

before the concrete sets, it crumbles. You have a mess to clean up and get to start over. This analogy illustrates what happens when you feel relief and improvement but stop the treatment regimen before your tissues fully heal and become strong.

Live It! How are you doing?

Take a minute to check yourself.

- Are your shoulders tight and climbing into your ears?
- How's your breathing? Are you breathing evenly—taking nice, slow, even breaths in and out? Is your breathing shallow with little chest movement and air-flow? Or you may be breathing rapidly, unevenly, and risking hyperventilation (bigger exhale breaths can result in tingling, tense hands and lips, dizziness, heart palpitations, or cold hands or feet.)

Now write down what you are thinking and feeling. Do you see a relationship between what you are thinking and feeling and your body's reactions? Then, let's build new, healthy habits to replace poor posture and reactive bad habits.

Building a Strong Physical Foundation

Practice these five helpful tips. Replace bad habits with healthy ones.

Live It! Proper Posture

1. Stand tall through the top and back of your head. Build up your trunk and core strength with consistency and correction. *Every time* you see red—stop lights, red Christmas décor, red, pink, or orange flowers, red objects around the house, and through your day—correct your posture and **practice**!
2. Pull your chin backward until your ear lobe aligns over the point of your shoulder.

3. Pull your shoulders down and back, like a ballet dancer. Send your heart to heaven.
4. Suck your belly button toward your mid-back to support your spine.
5. AND remember to breathe!

It takes about three weeks to three months to become comfortable with new, corrected postural habits. The time needed to make proper posture more comfortable than poor posture depends on how consistent you are with your correction and the severity of your problem.

Key Points and Summary

- **Seek professional help if you want it—even if you are not sure why.** Don't be afraid to get help and ask questions. Together, you and your provider can explore to find answers. Review the guidelines in the previous We All Need Advocacy section for health care shopping.
- **Write down your medical history and medication list to take to health care appointments.** You need to have an advance directive (a legal document that states your desires for your end-of-life medical care) like a living will or other legal forms. This document has no power after your death. If you have a health care Advocate (*one* person only for legal decisions), they need these written documents and your Medical Power of Attorney.
- **Understand how your body expresses what you believe and feel.** Our physical, mental, emotional, and spiritual components are intricately intertwined. Learn your body's language.
- **Remember to B-M-W.** Breathe-Melt (like butter; relax muscles from the top of your head to the tips of your toes)-Wiggle. Please review the Food For Thought section, and practice B-M-W to manage

stress and pain. The more you keep your mind clear, stay calm, and B-M-W, the better you feel and respond to a situation.

- **Practice proper posture.** Posture is the foundation for structural health, movement, and function. Proper posture fits each individual's gender, specific build, and body. Correct alignment is appropriate for every person.
- **Be *consistent* to achieve your goals.** Some people think poor posture is genetically hereditary. That is a myth. Poor postural habits develop through laziness, learning from others, or lack of understanding. Children often mimic parental example. You can improve your posture, strengthen your core, and prevent spinal problems with correction and consistency.
- **Ask, don't force.** As you correct your posture, build tissue strength, and balance, *ask*—don't force the corrections. You should feel work, not pain. You have the right to say, "Stop," to caregivers when you have questions or feel discomfort.
- **Recognize your unique design.** Our Creator designed and made each of us. Do you want to experience the most joy, stress relief, and peace in this life? Be the best you!
- **Listen to your Designer and Maker.** If you don't have a personal relationship with the Creator of all, please hear me: God didn't come to earth to make bad people better. He came to save and bring spiritually dead people like us to *life*! I'm not talking about a man-made religion or a system of making yourself good enough to deserve paradise. Experience the restorative healing power of our Creator. Receive profound peace and indescribable joy through hard times and good times by letting your Creator guide, protect, and provide. Keep reading and contact me at Bonnie@4x4Healing.com to learn more.

PART TWO
YOUR BODY SPEAKS

Thank You for making me so wonderfully complex! Your workmanship is marvelous—how well I know it.
Psalm 139:14

You never know yourself till you know more than your body.
Thomas Traherne

For life is more than food, and your body more than clothing.
Luke 12:23

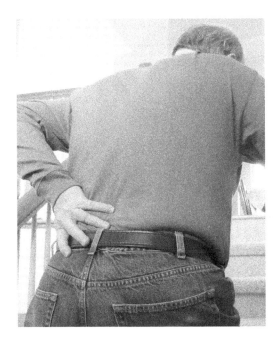

SECTION 1

DO YOU KNOW?

CHAPTER 9

Friend, Foe, or Stranger: Get To Know Yourself

How do you see your body? Is it your friend or enemy? Do you even recognize it as part of you?

Some folks pamper their bodies, valuing physical appearance as most important. Others take their bodies for granted. They perform physically demanding or prolonged work day after day without attention to rest-work balance. They ignore the fact their bodies need care.

One woman said she saw her body as a "tool." When she looked at the analogy more closely, she decided her pain and symptoms indicated she habitually neglected her body's care. She expected her body to endure long hours of standing and hard work without rest, movement, or attention. In effect, she left her "tool" out in the rain and weather, rusting and deteriorating. Through treatment, she learned to treat her body more like a baby. Just as a baby needs care and loving attentiveness, she gave her body priority and consistent attention, which allowed it to heal and return to full function.

> When you are physically injured or depleted, your body is vulnerable and performs at a younger level than your actual years.

The baby analogy works well when considering your physical needs. A child needs regular rest, food, safe activity, and healthy touch to grow and flourish. Without these elements, the child's overall health and function suffer. Listen to and nurture your body as you would a child. Your body performs according to your actual age when you provide for your physical needs—healthy fuel, balanced work and rest, and good hygiene. When you are physically injured or depleted, your body performs at a vulnerable level, younger than your actual years. Neglected bodies have less tolerance to stress, less ability to recover, and require more time and help to heal. Depending on how severe the neglect over time, your body will need tender care and consistent protection to return to age-appropriate function.

A woman (who we will call Mary) wrestled with pain, fibromyalgia, and limited function for years. She was active and tried many treatment approaches without resolution. Frustrated by the persistent pain and restrictions, Mary felt irritated because she wasn't getting better.

As we worked together, this woman, in her 40s, learned to see her body as a young child. Due to her pain and symptoms, Mary needed to pretend she had an infant permanently attached to her. Every time she *started* to feel pain, she remembered that her "baby" (body) needed care.

Babies need food and rest. For her body, the "baby rest" was *good quality rest*—not finger-drumming, impatient, "busy-brain" kind of rest where pressures and "shoulds" swirl around in your head while you struggle to sit still for a moment. You can't get good quality rest while watching TV or movies either. Your emotions, physical reactions to the story and action, and sitting upright create demands on your body.

For Mary, learning how to rest meant she needed to recognize and release muscle tension. She had to look at physical and non-physical contributors to her stress and tension levels—from past and present. It was important for Mary to "feed" (care for) her "baby" body. She learned how to use techniques such as numbing cold, adjusting her mental expectations temporarily, and changing her daily routine according to the specific independent home program (IHP) prepared for her by me as her physical therapist.

Mary followed her IHP consistently and learned to "listen" to her body. She imagined her body as a tiny child needing frequent food and rest. While Mary's mind expected her body to be functional, pain-free, and active, her body only had an infant's strength and endurance. This shocked Mary because she was an *adult* with things to do and felt she should function as an adult. But her physical reality allowed her to work without pain for only 30-60 minutes. Then, she needed to rest for the *same* amount of time and use her ice packs for ten minutes during each rest period.

After a couple of treatment and training sessions, Mary reported continued tiredness, dizziness, and pain. When I asked her how she was doing with her specific IHP, she said she did her ice as instructed once per day. When I asked her if she thought a baby would do well on one meal per day, the light came on. "Ooohhh," she said, "I hav-en't been feeding my baby enough to grow up!" We reviewed the performance and consistency of her specific IHP, how to evaluate the quality of her rest, and what changes to make. As Mary cared for her body, she steadily improved. She consistently rested and "fed" her body with massage, specific gentle movement, and numbing cold to increase circulation, reduce pain, and stop muscle spasms.

When Mary started rehabilitation, we decided her body's tolerances equaled an infant less than one-year-old. As she improved, the pain decreased in intensity, frequency, and duration. Her pain-free activity increased. Mary's body's age—the

> Note: An Independent Home Program (IHP) is a protocol of exercise, self-care, and retraining prepared by the physical therapist specifically for an individual patient. These instructions include frequency and technique to do the exercises and daily activities properly, using the right muscles to achieve desired results. An IHP provides systematic monitoring for physical, functional, and lifestyle improvement. These written instructions remind and encourage the patient to change through consistently performing daily living activities in the best way so that healthy changes become permanent.

"baby's" age and tolerances—matured to a two-year-old level, then a five-year-old level, then twelve, and eventually to an adult. Mary's body now functioned at the tolerance and performance level appropriate to her age and desired activity level. Recognizing the underlying emotional, mental, and spiritual contributors to her nagging pain also aided in permanently resolving her symptoms and limitations.

Through training and treatment, Mary learned her body language. She was able not only to listen to her body, but also to appropriately respond to her body's needs.

ઝ ઝ ઝ ઝ ઝ

A young man (we will call Jim) came into the clinic. Jim wanted to run marathons but wasn't able to train. Diagnosed with fibromyalgia and chronic fatigue, he tried multiple treatment approaches without success. Openly, he told me about his struggles, lifestyle, and goals. Then, I asked him to describe when things changed.

In sharing, Jim recognized when symptoms started and worsened gradually over time. Through Jim's physical therapy care, he realized the subtle, persistent stresses that had built up and affected his body. His physical therapy treatment included examining how his thinking affected his physical condition. The constant seemingly small pressures beneath the periodic, huge, "emergency" demands at work weighed on his mind, body, spirit, and emotions. He determined to resolve the underlying hindrances to his life and function by willingly exploring past hurts. Some of the questions Jim considered were:

- Am I pushing myself to prove something because of a past injury or relationship?
- Have I ever felt safe, valued, or content?
- What is the quality of my rest?
- What would *healed* look like for me?
- Do I *want* to be healed?

Jim also needed to look at his motives for running: Is he trying to escape, or enjoy the view, the fresh air, and time to think? Is he able to be still and enjoy quiet time? How is his work-rest balance?

Through treatment, Jim learned to change his thinking and choices. His thinking and actions became proactive instead of reactive. By attending to the condition of his body, and the underlying contributors from mind, heart, and spirit, this young man was able to heal completely. Physical pain and symptoms ceased. Jim returned to running marathons with a healthy work-rest balance—running for joy instead of away from hurts.

CHAPTER 10

Your Body Remembers: You Can Move From Hurt To Healed

Your body remembers and expresses your mental, emotional, and spiritual condition, whether you perceive it or not. Physical ailments may prompt us to seek medical care before we recognize or address non-physical contributors.

For those who have experienced childhood abuse and trauma, there may be a dissociative distance (a loss or gap of recognition and connection) between body and mind. Dissociation is a valuable and effective survival mechanism for dealing with overwhelming situations. In instances of sexual abuse or overwhelming physical trauma, a person may become numb or mentally separated from the body part that was injured or unprotected.

Some of my patients have been so distant from their physical body that they felt they don't exist. To lesser degrees, it is common for people to be out of touch with their bodies or not understand how to listen to their bodies.

Pain and problems will not resolve if we treat only the physical or the mental and ignore other contributors to the condition.

I have journeyed the healing path with several patients who felt separated or distant from their physical bodies. A patient who became a friend of mine wrote the following:

Dear Bonnie,

Thank you so very much for your gift of caring and sensitivity to me. When I first heard reports of your work from a friend, I was impressed. She said you treated her with genuine concern and respect as a person, not just another patient. But it was too hard to believe that there was someone I could trust with my special needs as a survivor of SRA (Satanic Ritual Abuse) and DID (Dissociative Identity Disorder). When injury forced me to need the help of a physical therapist, you seemed my safest option. It was your sensitive approach and honoring me with respect that gained my trust and gave me the courage to begin disclosing my history of abuse.

To my amazement, you have helped not only with my physical pain, but with my emotional healing as well. Allowing and often encouraging me to say, "No" and "Stop, that's enough" has given me a new sense of control over my body. Strange as it sounds, that was a difficult, even frightening new experience. But by practicing with you, I can now have the confidence to begin placing safe boundaries in other areas of my life where passive acceptance had left me feeling devalued and disrespected.

Discovering areas of my body that still carry the effects of trauma has helped me face those experiences. With that, I have begun moving through my inner healing process quicker and more efficiently. I have discovered reasons I react as I do and have been able to grieve my loss, finally letting go of some of the inner pain I've carried all these years. One benefit is that I can sometimes accept and enjoy safe, caring touch, and return the same to those I love. I am now much more in touch with my body and able to recognize what I need. I can relax more, enjoying day to day life with less pain—not just physically but emotionally and spiritually as well.

Thank you for this gift. —signed (my patient and friend)

If you identify with some of these feelings or experiences, help and healing are available. You don't need to be alone in your recovery. Ask for help from a trustworthy, insightful, and sensitive professional. Look for caring, *safe* family or friends who will encourage, protect, and support you during your healing journey. Don't be robbed of your potential and joy. Don't let wounds fester, grow, or hinder your function and relationships. Comprehensive healing brings benefits beyond your imagination.

CHAPTER 11
Technology Woes: Are You In Control?

Both the development and proliferation of technology have increased and introduced a variety of challenges. We have grown more dependent on outside sources for self-management, medical evaluation, and symptom resolution. At the same time, we are less able to recognize our abilities to deal with discomforts and health needs.

Technology brings time and energy savings, along with a distinct set of new problems. Cases of neck, back, carpal tunnel syndrome, and other upper body troubles explode in proportion to increased hours at the computer or on mobile devices. There is now a formal diagnosis of "texting neck" for neck and shoulder pain resulting from poor postural positions while using your phone. In most cases, these physical problems can be corrected without surgery.

Technology occupies a significant portion of our time and attention. The focus on smart phones, smart TVs, electronic pads, and computers for email, faxes, internet games, shopping, news, work, and information drastically reduces face-to-face communication. When you get together with family or friends, do you see faces? Are you connecting eye-to-eye, or is each person focused on what they have in their hands?

The consequences of reduced human interaction are generations who lack social skills, strike back violently in stressful situations, and fail to practice respect, courtesy, self-control, and manners. In recent years, researchers have seen a steady decline in the ability to problem-solve, recognize options, and exercise restraint. The void in one-to-one interaction affects us neurologically, relationally, and physically.

Research confirms[6] the increase in teen suicide with the proliferation of smart phones, computer games, and technology addictions[7]. Just look around you. When was the last time you saw people focused on each other instead of a device? Time previously allocated to face-to-face interaction over past decades now focuses on isolated device usage. Technology has invaded and conquered our workspace, leisure, and home life.

Medical Impact

As in all growing industries, technology use in the medical field is increasing. What happens when attention focuses on test results without balanced support from the patient's history and exam? Test results have a powerful influence—even though they can be *inaccurate*. Tests need to confirm and quantify patient history and physical evidence.

Do you know that you can question test results and the diagnosis you receive? The medical staff is there for you. So, if something doesn't sound right or if you have questions, use your voice to ask for a clear explanation. Good medical practice means focused listening to the patient, careful observation, insightful assessment of physical and non-physical elements, and explaining test results.

Manipulated Desires

The constant bombardment of advertisements manipulates our desires and distorts reality. Undesirable elements of human nature (such as envy, greed, and covetous feelings) have always been there—we either feed or starve these self-centered tendencies.

Before the technological age, negative feelings of comparison were more localized—such as "keeping up with the Joneses" in your neighborhood. Today, media bombardment plants wide-spread comparison and discontent. Do we need a new medication, more clothes, or a better version of what we already have? The focus on what we *don't have* instead of the blessings that we *do have* leads us to believe that the next purchase, relationship, or desire attained will solve festering discontent.

Social media feeds this deception. Our online world show-cases beautiful places, smiling faces, and happy spaces. However, these images don't tell the whole story. If you base your happiness on this unbalanced superficial perspective, you get caught in constant comparison. You think then feel what others have is better and more than what you have. You drive yourself into a perpetual self-focused pity party. Prejudice erupts from this self-focused victim identity. "Comparison discontent" destroys joy, peace, unity, rest, and thankfulness.

৶৶ ৶৶ ৶৶ ৶৶ ৶৶

Body, mind, emotions, and spirit are intimately connected. Anger, depression, internal conflict, and other churning emotions often manifest physically as skin rashes, arthritis flares, gastrointestinal upsets, headaches, cardiac problems, and chronic pain conditions.

On the other hand, positive attitudes such as gratitude and contentment build your immune system, decrease stress, and counter negative emotions. Gratitude results in peace, rest, contentment, and joy beyond circumstances.[8]

> Focusing on what you *don't* have leads to depression. Being grateful for what you *do have* fuels deep peace, contentment, and joy.

Do you appreciate loved ones and supportive friends? Are you thankful when waking to a beautiful day, breathing fresh air deeply, savoring delicious tastes, feasting on lovely colors, or standing in awe at the glory of a night sky full of stars? Look for and value the good things in life—small and large.

We are created for relationship, for human interaction. Loss of verbal and non-verbal communication and social connection disrupts sleep, feeds depression, and suffocates joy. Eye-to-eye connection with another person communicates volumes. Six times per second, encouraging non-verbal information is shared eye-to-eye, feeding your "joy center" (the right orbital prefrontal cortex of your brain). Face-to-face smiles and joyful tones radiate messages of "I'm happy to see you" and cause your joy center to grow. The harsh tones, frowns, and the absence of smiles shrink your joy center.

As technology attention replaces relationship time, your joy fades, and relational skills erode. Loss of human interaction promotes egocentric thinking, impatience, and isolation. Blaming God or others for your misery allows bitterness, resentment, anger, and fears to ruminate inside. These powerful negative emotions increase your stress and cortisol levels, which can feed cancer, increase headaches, aggravate digestive problems, cause rashes, and other physical pathology.

CHAPTER 12

No Quick Fix: Do You Want To Be Healed?

Technology feeds instant gratification in our society. The growing expectation of a quick fix creates feelings of entitlement, impatience, selfishness, and unrealistic demands. Demanding that our desires be met instantly promotes the false perception that we can't wait, or our own needs are more important than the needs of others. I have asked myself, "How patient are you when in traffic jams, standing in line, or waiting for your computer to respond?" My selfish impatience was revealed.

This quick-fix thinking affects how we view healing. Even when ill or injured, we feel we should be pain-free, have enough energy to get up and go to work, meet our deadlines, take care of the house and kids, and live as actively as our minds imagine. This quick-fix deception hinders rather than helps our healing.

$$\partial\!\!\!/\!\!\!\ell \quad \partial\!\!\!/\!\!\!\ell \quad \partial\!\!\!/\!\!\!\ell \quad \partial\!\!\!/\!\!\!\ell \quad \partial\!\!\!/\!\!\!\ell$$

While enjoying time with our daughter, I strained my back doing activities I had not performed in years. I enjoyed feeling younger than my years, remembering my gymnastics days. I felt great until I woke up the next morning—and could hardly stand up. I cared for myself as I would have cared for my family or a patient. And like many of my patients, I became impatient. I wanted to be back to full function in days, not weeks. I had to *stop* and reflect on the facts. I reminded myself that healing required time and to implement consistent self-care. I recognized that the current needs of my body were more important than the demands in my head. My impatience ceased (with repeated reminders). I chose to be consistent and patient. I did have a couple of setbacks because I felt better and did too much too soon, so it took me eight weeks to heal from this severe strain.

During recovery, the riskiest time is when you start to feel good after an injury. The danger of re-injury is high because you think you can be more active than your body can tolerate.

Compare the healing process to pouring concrete. After you pour concrete into a frame, you need time for it to set. If you remove the supporting structures too soon, the concrete cracks and crumbles, leaving a mess to clean up. Then, you need to start over. When you begin to feel good after injury, continue your prescribed consistent care for at least two weeks *after* the symptoms cease before you stop.

❧ ❧ ❧ ❧ ❧

We live in a wonderful time. Some medications provide a long-term cure, and some provide temporary pain relief, which satisfies our innate desire for a quick fix. They are easily accessible, act quickly, cover up the cause of the pain, and give a false sense of well-being. Don't let medical "cover-up" keep you from correcting the causes of your pain and problems.

Take time to ask questions and explore other treatment options.

Example Questions:

1. What goals do you have for using medications?
2. Will the medication solve your problem, cause cascading side-effects and complications, or create unnecessary expense? It's easy to overlook possible side-effects that can lead to other issues that result in additional prescriptions.

3. Are there drug-free options to manage or solve the problems you face?
4. Are you willing to try a drug-free approach to resolve your issue?
5. When will you be able to get off the medication?

Having support from others can encourage you if that quick fix state of mind pushes you into depression or discouragement. You achieve more efficient and satisfying healing when you receive follow-up feedback and encouragement.

Regular treatment:

1. Keeps you on track by providing both direction and encouragement
2. Reveals and tracks your progress or stagnation
3. Reminds you to do your Independent Home Program (IHP) properly and consistently

Consistency and teamwork are the most effective and efficient elements in achieving lasting improvement.

CHAPTER 13

Healthy Change Requires Both Physical & Mental Retraining: Unlearn So You Can Learn

When a college student (who we will call Kat) came to see me, she reported various physical pains that began concurrently with a rigorous new dance schedule. Even though these classes' requirements and activities were new to her, she built strength (instead of being injured through her demanding classes) with proper warm-ups, alignment and technique training, and support.

Along with physical training and rehabilitation, Kat needed to consider her beliefs and goals. Will she take personal responsibility to complete the training and treatment? Does she believe she can heal? Are her goals and expectations realistic? Will she commit to the weeks or months it may take to heal?

Kat, like many of us, became impatient with the time it took to heal and recover. She was aware that bone healing takes about twelve weeks in a healthy individual (without complications). Kat's injuries were to ligaments—connecting bone to bone—and tendons—connecting muscle to bone. These soft tissues require at least six weeks to heal and then additional time to gain strength. Kat's injuries took longer to recover because she used the injured tissues every day in school.

Added to the strains and minor injuries Kat sustained during her strenuous physical demands, she carried an intense academic and recreational schedule. Therefore, she was fatigued. When Kat started to feel better, she believed she should be able to function at full throttle without pain or fatigue. This desire and viewpoint are common—but not realistic. You need time to catch up with rest, strength, and endurance after an injury.

Think of it this way: Picture your energy as water in a bucket. When you are healthy and have a good work-rest balance, your bucket has enough water (energy) to carry you through the day. But when you are injured or depleted, your bucket has a few holes in the bottom. You fill the bucket with water. As you go through each task of the day, you steadily lose water (energy) through the holes. The amount of water in the bucket is insufficient for your desired work or recreation.

As you gain strength and energy, carefully monitor your activity. It is very easy to pile one event on another and forget how much you do throughout the day. Many common injuries occur from accumulated demands, not just one activity. Proper rest is critical for healing.

> Good quality rest is necessary for healing and is a shield against physical, mental, emotional, and spiritual stress.

Remember, the most dangerous time in your recovery happens when you first feel good because you tend to overdo and stop following your IHP. As pain diminishes and limitations evaporate, you tend to return to your previous routines quickly, causing reinjury.

For lasting improvement, listen to your body, provide plenty of excellent rest, gentle, appropriate movement, and be consistent in your IHP for a few weeks after all your pain and symptoms have ceased.

SECTION 2
FOOD FOR THOUGHT

CHAPTER 14

Rest is a Weapon: Be Your Best With Rest

A patient (whom we will call Donna) came to see me complaining of dizziness and pain in her neck. After evaluating and treating vertigo and her painful upper body, Donna received an individualized IHP to correct physical maladies and to remind her to make appropriate changes in her daily activities. Her vertigo ceased, and she felt better.

One of the main factors in her IHP was not visible during her evaluation. I recognized this subtle problem only when listening to her history. Donna shared her life activities and stresses over the last few weeks. She stated that she was sleeping for eight hours per night, but still felt tired most of the time. I questioned the balance between her work and her rest. Then, I asked what was going on in her mind during the day and when she went to bed.

This woman feverishly worked at home and on the job. She lifted, carried, climbed, and did substantial physical activity every day. Concern over finances, her children, and taking care of her home and family drove her all day long. Donna continually rehearsed phrases like, "It's my responsibility," and, "If I don't do this, no one will." She held a hidden belief that if she really rested, she was being lazy. She expected to be able to do everything she desired or felt pressured to do. Whatever sleep she got should be sufficient to refresh her, resolve pain, and re-energize her entirely. At bedtime, Donna focused on the things she hadn't accomplished during the day, what she needed to do the next day, financial concerns, her children's problems, and what she should have done differently to improve her relationships. Donna exhausted herself day and night.

Like Donna, do you mentally rework your day, words, choices, and relationships at the end of the day when it is time for sleep? Or maybe your busy brain continues to churn your worries, what others might think of you, your financial challenges, and your daunting "to do" list into one big stew. Do you have trouble saying "no" appropriately when people ask you to do something? Do you struggle to make yourself sleep? Can you receive and savor rest and quiet times? Can you relate to those pressures? I can, too.

When you have trouble sleeping, do you turn on the lights, get out of bed, or watch TV? Those habits interrupt the normal sleep cycle, which makes it even harder to establish a nighttime sleep pattern. Insomnia results from many sources, but there are some basic techniques you can try. If your mind reruns what happened during the day or tosses and turns about your future, your sleep will most likely be fitful, interrupted, and not restful. Endlessly revisiting past wounds or projecting future unknowns leads to distorted perspectives, wasted time, and exhausted energy.

 Check out the Appendix: *Fatigue and Negative Thought Progressions*

Lies, harbored hurts, and depressing thoughts are like gnats that fly around your head. You swat at these tiny, irritating insects, but they continue to hover in a cloud around your face and head. Just like gnats, negative thoughts become more annoying and prevalent.

When you get caught up in thoughts of past hurts and future "what ifs," you activate the Fear-Tension-Pain Cycle, elevate your cortisol levels, and cultivate feelings of worry, defensiveness, and threat. You lose the peace of the moment and sacrifice true rest and joy.

Have you heard the saying, "The past is history, the future is a mystery, and today is a present—a gift given by God"? Don't miss the peace, rest, joy, and hidden blessing that He provides in *the moment*—look for it. Our Creator sees a much bigger picture and purpose than we can imagine. He asks us to trust Him through life's pain and challenges.

ॐ ॐ ॐ ॐ ॐ

In the 1970s and 1980s, western culture's message to women was, "You can do it all and have it all." That message, and the cultural trends, seeped into my brain telling me that I was invincible. I could be an attentive wife, a sensitive mom, a successful professional, and run my own two-office business without any help or problems. It sounded great but was totally unrealistic.

One day, while dressed in my business suit for an important meeting, I looked down at our infant daughter in her carrier on my arm. She looked at me nervously, sucking furiously on her pacifier. Friends said they could feel the intense energy radiating from me when they were around me. That was not good because I had no stillness or peace in me. In this unbalanced condition, I was not at my best—for me, my family, or my patients.

However, my life changed for the better. I'll tell you how in an upcoming chapter.

> I cannot give to others what I do not possess myself.

Dave, a hard-working professional, taught me a valuable lesson. As with many of my patients, I learn from them as I hope they learn from me. Simply stated, he dropped this pearl of wisdom one day during one of his physical therapy sessions:

He said, "I know what our problem is."

"Oh?" I responded. "What is our problem?"

This astute patient responded, "We don't know when we are tired."

I felt like I'd been struck by lightning. I had never recognized that fact, but it was true. My automatic internal message was, "I have to finish the job." I lived and believed I could always do more—faster, farther, harder, higher. It was a routine I never questioned. I stayed late at the clinic and took work home. At home, I cared for home and family—and did clinic preparation and paperwork. I would stay up late and get up early. I never recognized my fatigue symptoms.

Because of Dave, I learned to tune into my body's fatigue messages—how they were different from feeling energized. I understood how being overtired causes me to be impatient and distant from my family.

It may sound strange that I didn't know how fatigue felt, but you only understand your own experience until you encounter new information. I learned how to listen to the needs of my body, mind, and spirit. I found and practiced healthy work-rest balance, changed some boundaries, and explored better options.

Another sign of fatigue can be mental wandering. When I was overtired, I often reread material several times before I grasped it, and my memory wasn't sharp. When fatigue took its toll, my focus became cloudy, and I felt directionless. However, when I listened to my body's warnings and rested, these symptoms ceased. Yet, I didn't comprehend the cultural lie I embodied—I am woman, I can do it all—until I *chose* to heal. It was then I learned how to rest completely.

❧ ❧ ❧ ❧ ❧

Rest does not equal sleep. Physical, mental, and emotional fatigue affects us in several negative ways. Prolonged stress and demands at work, caused by our choices or pressure from others, often result in burnout. Can this same condition happen at home, in daily life? Absolutely! Physical, mental, and emotional exhaustion can lead to impatience, depression, cynicism, detachment, and fear. A lack of quality rest sneaks up on you gradually. It results from accumulated stress over time, though episodes of intense demand will accelerate the condition.

The terms "sleep" and "rest" are used interchangeably in research literature. Studies indicate that people who regularly skimp on sleep may start to show signs of biochemical and metabolic changes that can lead to dementia and other diseases.[9]

So, what are some of the signs of *rest deprivation* or burnout? Remember—everyone briefly experiences some of these symptoms at times. Symptoms of emotional, mental, and physical exhaustion are uniquely individual and vary in degree and expression. This list is not for diagnosing, just indicators for you to consider or report to your health care provider. Since rest depletion comes on slowly, tune in to the warning signs so you can monitor your rest-work balance.

When you suffer from a long-term lack of rest:

1. You feel tired more days than you feel energetic. You dread getting out of bed, going to work, or facing the chores of the day. You feel ineffective, slow, and drained most days.
2. You lose JOY. You don't feel deep contentment or ecstatic joy. You forget what excited you in the past, like hobbies, hikes, playing a musical instrument, or fun with family or friends.
3. You are irritable and impatient. A good fatigue indicator is impatience with people and situations.
4. You have trouble sleeping—initially, you struggle to get to sleep or stay asleep a couple of times a week. Insomnia then progresses to a nightly problem, robbing you of even more sleep and rest, and becomes a difficult habit to break. In chronic insomnia, other medical influences may be present, so consider getting a professional examination.
5. You lack mental focus—you feel mentally slow or foggy, you have trouble concentrating, or become more forgetful.
6. You experience physical symptoms— headaches, heart palpitations, chest tightness, shortness of breath, dizziness, fainting spells, digestive system pain, or other physical problems.[10]

Isolation is a natural response to exhaustion. Misleading feelings of pain, blame, victimization, anger, resentment, bitterness, hopelessness, doubt, and depression grow in isolation. Persistent lie messages and churned up emotions eventually interfere with rational thinking, decision making, and personal relationships.

Physical, mental, and emotional fatigue over time impacts all human systems. Subtly and slowly, without notice, your thoughts and attention become more emotional and self-oriented. You receive and interpret messages that build defensiveness and threat reactions. You emotionally react instead of thinking clearly and responding (being in control of yourself, your choices, and actions). Extreme and prolonged internal focus can result in paranoia, isolation, and perceived victimization.

Emotional, reactive choices give control to others. Rational, responsive living restores control to you.

I enjoyed reading Robert Ludlum's spy novels. In his book "The Bourne Identity," one principle stated by the spy character Jason Bourne stands out. This spy and his friend were running for their lives. Alone and hunted by a team of skilled adversaries, they had no help and no direction. They looked desperately for an escape route or place to hide from the killers chasing them. Consuming fear drove them to keep going, but Jason knew the dangers of fatigue and uncontrolled anxiety. He told his friend, "Sleep is a weapon." If they kept running without rest, they would make deadly mistakes. He knew that taking time to sleep, even at considerable risk, would help him and his friend think clearly, react more quickly, and give them the physical energy they needed to survive.

As I read this part of the book, the word sleep didn't register with me. My mind heard and retained, "*Rest* is a weapon." Sleep can bring refreshment, or you can awaken physically and mentally tired. Sleep can be restless or interrupted.

On the other hand, good quality rest occurs when you release your situation, worry, tension, pressures, and busy brain. Comprehensive rest also includes deep peace and trust in a dependable power beyond yourself. True rest promotes good quality sleep and restores your emotions, mind, spirit, and body.

As a young wife and mother, I hadn't learned to listen to my body. Therefore, I didn't know when I was tired and didn't take time to rest. I slowed down, but my mind remained active with the responsibility for my family, work, employees, and household demands. This prevented me from being most efficient in my work and giving my full attention to the people around me.

When Dave said, "We don't know when we are tired," I began paying attention to my fatigue symptoms and decided to make changes.

That decision involved a serious radical break in my schedule, changing my ingrained driven habits. I spent hours on my bedroom floor, practicing the active relaxation I taught my patients. I worked to melt deeper and deeper into the floor, intentionally turning off muscles that automatically wanted to tense into readiness for action. I purposely slowed and stretched my breathing. I deliberately focused on quieting my mind and being still. Writing down thoughts and feelings cleared my mind—like putting important ideas on a whiteboard to process later.

To this day, I have paper and pen or a voice recorder at my bedside to keep an active brain from stealing good quality rest and sleep. I set a timer to interrupt my work concentration so I go to bed at a reasonable hour. Now, it's much easier to listen to my body and respond quickly.

What are the signs that you need better quality rest?

Many factors cause fatigue. To correct insomnia and persistent fatigue, you need to know the causes. But first, you should recognize ten warning signs:

1. Moodiness, such as irritability
2. Falling asleep during your workday or at inappropriate times
3. Chronic tiredness or sleepiness

4. Impaired decision-making and judgment
5. Dizziness
6. Burning eyes, more difficulty focusing
7. Racing heart rate
8. Weakness or sore or aching muscles
9. Headache
10. Slowed reflexes and responses

Think about your regular physical and mental activity. How do you feel when you are alone, quiet, and still? If you are driven by the "shoulds" in life—internal or external—you probably need more quality rest.

When you deal with a demanding decision or crisis, worry, or feel unsafe, restorative rest is difficult. Take a moment to evaluate your work-rest balance:

Five elements of good quality, restorative rest include:

- *Deep peace* results from the ability to release anxiety, tension, and offenses into our Creator God's hands. Deep peace and contentment come from the knowledge and trust that God knows the plans He has for you, He knows how to care for those who belong to Him, and that He will get you through your problems.
- *Patience* is not finger-drumming, antsy waiting for things to work out in your way, in your time, according to your expectations. Patience found in healing rest completely releases time and results to God's will, Word, way, and time, knowing that He has the map and will lead you through difficulties in the best way.
- *Stillness*, which is the ability to be serenely still, relaxed, and quiet—it is foundational for excellent rest.
- *Unencumbered playtime* describes the ability to fully enjoy time with others (i.e., playing face-to-face board or card games, instead of electronic games which do not build joy because attention is on devices instead of interpersonal interaction and eye-to-eye contact).

- **Real laughter,** not just a giggle, snicker, or chuckle, but laughing so hard tears come! Times of full joy, positive connection, and belly laughing are *the best medicine* for body, mind, heart, and spirit.

Through evaluation and replacing unhealthy habits, you can improve your quality of rest, which will enhance your energy, clear thinking, and overall ability to get things done.

You can't create more time or even stretch time. So, we need to reorder our time to maximize energy, choices, and efficiency.

Joy-filled experiences (which touch body, mind, and soul) improve sleep, energy, stress management, mental and physical health.

How will you reprioritize your time by making *rest* your weapon?

"Always laugh when you can. It is cheap medicine."
LORD BYRON

"Laughter is the shortest distance between two people."
VICTOR BORGE

CHAPTER 15

Altered Perspectives: Choose Clarity Over Confusion

Your body speaks by reacting to physical demands, your emotional state, and what you believe. If you believe you can't, you most often can't. Studies show that when undergoing a surgical procedure, a patient who adopts a positive outlook, expresses confidence in the surgical team, trusts in God, and desires to heal, experiences a better outcome than those who feel hopeless, depressed, passive, and believe nothing will help.

Sometimes a Sneeze is Just a Sneeze

Think about an ordinary event you made into a big deal. Let me illustrate. I love horses, the smell of hay, working with the animals, and being outdoors. One day, while blowing out the aisle in the barn, I sneezed. My friend asked if I was allergic to hay or horses. She assumed my sneeze had to be related to an allergy, which would label my sneeze, give me a life sentence, and destroy my joy of horses and all that goes with them. My sneeze was just a "snapshot in time" from dust blowing around me.

Today, drug advertisements and sometimes the medical community interpret an innocuous snapshot as a serious diagnosis. Take time to evaluate your symptoms holistically. What is the truth? Is it simply a sneeze?

What is Normal?

Over the years, many patients expressed confusion about how *normal* should look and feel. Our culture promotes lies that life should be pain-free, effort-free, and problem-free. Society loves quick fixes. First, there is no such thing as a quick fix that skips the necessary steps and time. Second, life is a hike. Hiking requires problem-solving to plan, prepare, and find the best path. Each step requires you to choose, take action, manage discomfort, build camaraderie along the way, and endure with patience. A productive life requires exerting effort, coping with stress, and managing pain. However, there are times of relief, joy, rest, and refreshment. The next time you face difficult trials, remember this phrase: "It came to pass—it didn't come to stay."

Normal vs. Ideal

Though *normal* is difficult to quantify, there are basic principles to treasure and teach. A culture may *redefine normal* according to changing mores or current government standards. If *normal* means widespread or ordinary, then it happens routinely without much thought or effort. Let the chips fall where they may. But if *normal* means desirable, then it becomes an intentional goal. Therefore, desirable or ideal *normal* must be taught, learned, practiced, and protected.

Healthy, moral, and wise living is ideal-normal. If that is true—is shame-free, joy-filled, and purposeful life a real possibility? Or is it just an ethereal hope found only in dreamy stories?

Our Creator intended us to live ideal-normal lives. Hurts and problems come at us—allowed by God to show us our limitations and turn us to Him as our Father for help and guidance. When we live out our ideal-normal, there is no drama, little or no fear, and abundant peace and joy.

Children feel safe and free to learn, enjoy age-appropriate interactions, experience protective, healthy boundaries, and practice respect and selfless courtesy. As children grow to adulthood, they gain training and equipping to ask our Savior for wisdom and whatever is needed to face and systematically solve problems calmly. They have the support of healthy others to share their journey through joy, pain, and trials. Best of all, when they honor their Creator, they receive direction, confidence, peace, and strength beyond their own.

Ideal-normal people show respect by treating others as they want to be treated. They take personal responsibility for their choices and actions. However, they do not take responsibility for what is not in their sphere of authority. Constructive criticism is for problem-solving, correcting, and helping—never for punishing or shaming. There is no win-lose; there is only win-learn.

For survivors of abuse and domestic violence, these notions are foreign. In a world where rules, boundaries, selfless love, and forgiveness disappear, these concepts are elusive and confusing. When civil principles are understood and experienced, ideal-normal becomes compelling and provides safety, health, purpose, peace, contentment, and confidence.

If you've never experienced ideal-normal, realize that you can. The same God who created you replaces the past's pain and losses with blessings in the future. He desires to restore you fully. Yes, it takes time, but you can step into a new life with a healthy guide.

The first time you visit an unfamiliar land, you need a guide who knows the language, dangers, and wonderful sites. A knowledgeable, trustworthy coach guides you into ideal-normal life. It is never too late to move from pain to potential and from fearful to free.

Don't give up. Don't settle for less than God's best for you. This journey—where you learn, grow, exercise your true identity, serve others, build healthy relationships, and step into your God-given potential—becomes ideal-normal living.

Pay attention to your body so you can correct problems early. Start with your posture, which is your physical foundation. If you have pain, listen to your body so you can fix the cause or seek appropriate help.

Have you been surprised by physical discomforts? Too often, you don't recognize how much demand you put on your body every day or consider the effect of repetitive or cumulative exertion. The body grows stronger and builds resilience through physical demand, but there must be restorative rest and good food (fuel) to meet the needs.

> Life will never be pain-free. You will feel pain and have trouble as long as you are alive. The key is to manage the pain and the challenges in the wisdom, strength, and sufficiency of our Creator, Lord, and Savior, Jesus.

Here's a quick physical checklist:

- ☐ Do you repeatedly stay up late at night when you work during the day?
- ☐ Do you slouch with your head down while you peer at your phone or computer for long hours?
- ☐ Do you lift heavy objects with poor biomechanics?
- ☐ Do you stand still for the majority of a day with minimal movement and rest balance?

If you checked any of these items, expect to experience physical pain and fatigue.

So, what kind of sensations are *normal* and realistic?

Let's define *normal* as typical, usual, expected, or the standard state, functioning naturally without identifiable abnormalities or deficiencies. Without disease or abnormality, it is normal to feel periodic fleeting episodes of general body or muscle weakness due to fatigue. Rare transitory muscle soreness or nerve pain in any area of your body is also expected, especially after being sedentary, or after new, prolonged, or strenuous activity.

We'll define temporary as lasting less than three days and not recurring. Fleeting pain lasts seconds or up to a few minutes.

It's important to remember each person is unique. Also, we must consider possible pathologic conditions. Sensations, and the interpretation of those sensations, are very personal. If symptoms persist or recur, seek professional evaluation and treatment.

CHAPTER 16

But I Didn't Do Anything Unusual.
Be Sensitive To Your Needs

How many times do you feel soreness or see a bruise on yourself and think, "Where did that come from? I didn't do anything!"

Poor posture and faulty biomechanics contribute significantly to everyday aches and pains. To correct bad positional and movement habits, expect discomfort during the retraining process. This work soreness falls into the *good pain* category we discussed previously. Don't let short term discomforts rob you of long-term benefits.

Sandy came into the office complaining of low back pain, leg pain, and numbness. As an active woman with a full schedule, her previous treatment and training taught her to watch her posture and biomechanics.

When we reviewed her activities and lifestyle, she'd been standing, walking, and moving heavy objects for several weeks and now was sitting and driving most of the time. Her problems resolved quickly with one treatment, a specific IHP (Independent Home Program), and reminders to balance work and rest.

If you sit most of the time, keep your feet and hips dancing. Get up every couple of hours to get water or use the restroom. If you stand and move all day, take rest breaks—get off your feet.

Effective physical therapy combines physical rehabilitation with cognitive training.

After her doctor's appointment, Kathy came into the clinic seeking treatment for her knee pain. Previous corrective therapies and pain medication helped somewhat, but the pain in both knees increased. She felt helpless and hopeless. A young mother, she struggled to care for her three small children and home. After evaluating her condition and listening to her, we found the path to her healing. Like many people, Kathy was goal-oriented— focused and determined to finish the project or activity she started rather than take a break, pace the work, or attend to her physical needs.

Kathy lived in a tri-level home with three children under five years old. With knee alignment and biomechanical problems that needed treatment and retraining, she also had a minor strain that had turned into a compensation injury (using wrong muscles to accomplish function).

Doing her best to take care of her home and family, she didn't plan rest breaks into her schedule. Her goal was to finish every project she started. Every day, she had quite a long list of tasks to accomplish. She didn't consider stopping halfway through cleaning the house, driving, shopping, or laundry duties.

After recognizing how many times she went up and down the stairs, Kathy realized she could take breaks before finishing tasks. She made both mental and priority adjustments. For instance, Kathy installed a hook high up on the inside of the children's room door so she could lie down in the room with the kids, close her eyes, and rest for a few moments. Even though the children made noise and climbed on her, those few minutes of knowing they were safe gave Kathy a chance to let go and get quality rest.

In a healthy state, you don't notice muscle tension, breathing changes, or heart rate fluctuations. But when depleted or injured, you may be surprised by discomfort during regular activities.

Stress builds you up or breaks you down.

Consider your physical activities and the cumulative effect of your daily demands. Remember that stress builds you up or breaks you down, depending on how you deal with your physical, mental, or emotional stress. Listen to your body. Maintain work-rest balance appropriate to your current physical condition and examine your automatic reactions to stress.

Most injuries do not result from a single traumatic event. Common non-traumatic injuries are due to repetition and accumulated stresses, such as deficient rest, poor posture, improper biomechanics, or prolonged new activity without adequate preparation and training. Learn to listen to your body. Avoid being sedentary or overdoing.

SECTION 3

LET'S DO THIS!

CHAPTER 17

Helpful Tips for You to Practice: Your Healing Is One "Rep" at a Time

Have you experienced fleeting, shooting nerve pain? These zingers are like a sneeze. Their cause is not clear, but if you practice relaxation and B-M-W, these minor shooting nerve irritations resolve, usually within seconds. On the other hand, a nervous tic, can be stress-related and can continue for minutes or days. The management is the same:

- Practice B-M-W frequently
- Listen to the needs of your body
- Get adequate, good quality rest.

If problems persist, get professional help.

When I am overtired, I occasionally experience a racing heartbeat. It can be unnerving, so I make B-M-W my first response. I actively relax my shoulders, jaw, and body as I rest, which successfully slows my heart rate within two to ten minutes. Fear only exacerbates the problem. It's not easy to truly B-M-W—slow your breathing evenly in and out, melt like butter deeply into your mattress or chair, and gently wiggle your legs, hips, shoulders, and head. But B-M-W becomes more automatic with practice. If the symptoms continue and you cannot replace your anxiety with relaxation, seek help but keep practicing B-M-W.

It's time to put your new knowledge to work: REST

Live It! Track your rest habits.

Keep an activity and rest diary to realistically see your work/ rest ratios and make appropriate corrections for healing and general good health. Written records are beneficial for several reasons. Track the amount and type of activity on a calendar or dated journal to:

1. Help you and your provider monitor progress and adjust your plan according to your needs and tolerances
2. Help you recognize your limitations and clarify goals
3. Increase your ownership and acceptance of the time needed for healing and change
4. Dissipate your impatience and discouragement.
5. See steady improvement and remember how far you have come

Live It! Change your thought patterns

1. Stop the busy-brain negative-thought progression by writing down everything going through your head. In other words, swat those gnats on to paper! Get all your thoughts and feelings out of your head and on paper. Leave them there until you are well-rested, can think clearly, and can share with wise, caring others. Then, take time to examine the facts, problem-solve, and evaluate realistic options for each concern you listed.
2. B-M-W to quiet your brain as you write down your churning thoughts and feelings.
3. Go to sleep when you have left everything on paper. With every breath, exhale and sink deeper and deeper into the mattress. Slowly tense your muscles and then let go—sink deeply into the bed. Continue practicing this active relaxation to train your body and your mind to let go.

4. Get socks or microwavable booties to warm your feet and your bed to help you relax.
5. Remedy any minor or major discomfort. You'll go to sleep faster when you're cozy and comfortable.

After you are rested and can think clearly, question the messages you receive and believe. Assess your condition to see where to make improvements. Share perspectives with trustworthy people. *Accepting ideas and messages without question* and *settling for less than what is best* is easy and common.

Live It! Assess your sleep patterns

1. *Judge Your Sleepiness.* Do you doze off during normal awake hours? Ask your family or friends to verify the accuracy of your perceptions. You can use the *Epworth Sleepiness Scale* for a more quantitative measurement.[11]
2. *Evaluate Your Performance.* Have you noticed deficits at work, school, or athletic training? If you are not as efficient, not thinking as clearly, or slowing down, you might want to increase your sleep to remedy those deficits. Record (on a calendar or log) when you get to sleep and the time you awaken to realistically determine your sleep amounts and patterns.
3. *Schedule a Vacation.* When did you last unplug from your routine? Get away for at least one week to someplace relaxing and enjoyable. Go to a place where you can sleep as long as you want.
4. *Exercise regularly.* Once rested, get out, take a walk, a swim, a bike ride. You will sleep better and get a better feel for work-rest pacing if you get up, get dressed, meet the day, and get your circulation going and muscles moving.

Live It! What's your ideal-normal?

1. On paper, draw a line down the middle to make two columns. At the top of the first column, write, "What is

working in my life."Think about desirable relationships, improved situation, healthy changes, joys, etc. Over the second column, write, "What is *not* working in my life." What are the troubling thoughts, difficult relationships, harmful habits, and physical pains you want to correct?

2. On another piece of paper, list what you want to keep in your life and what you want to change.

3. List how you can change for the better and what is out of your control.

4. Find a healthy coach, pastor, or health professional who *lives* the way you want to live. Ask that person to journey with you into a new, fuller life.

Head and Neck

Headaches can result from muscle tension, fatigue, caffeine, stress, smoke or air pollution, bright light, wearing glasses, blood pressure or vascular problems, past trauma, clenching or grinding your teeth, and more causes than we can list here. Headaches can vary in intensity, frequency, and duration from once or twice per year, lasting from few minutes to migraine headaches occurring daily and functionally paralyzing the sufferer.

A common source of headaches is poor postural alignment and muscle tension. There are new diagnoses caused by prolonged poor head and neck posture while using handheld technology.

Look around as you go through your day. Observe the head, neck, and shoulder position of other people. How do they habitually use their phones or computers, drive, do paperwork, watch TV, etc.? Check your position. Evaluate how your position feels. Review proper posture and alignment, the foundation, as discussed in previous chapters and the Appendix.

Live It! Headache Treatment

Put your fingers on your forehead and move the skin around. Is there any pain, or do you only feel the pressure of your fingers? Does the skin move easily, without pain, about half the width of your fingertip? That is the desirable norm, not only for your forehead but also for your scalp. Now, put your fingers on your head and move the muscles and skin of your scalp. Most often, your scalp tissues are less mobile and more tender than your forehead.

Ideally, your scalp will be as mobile as your forehead and not be sensitive or tender to massage. If you suffer headaches, here are some simple but important things you can do to attend to your body and prevent headaches. You can use some or all of these techniques and in any order:

1. *Correct your posture!* Correct posture is the essential aspect of lasting improvement. Retract your chin backward toward your neck, then pull your shoulders down out of your ears. Be consistent! Writing the reasons you want to improve your posture (such as relieving pain, looking better, feeling better, improving breathing and digestion, preventing headaches and arthritis, etc.) will remind you to practice and keep you motivated. Review the information about proper posture and alignment. Remember, proper posture is the foundation of position and movement. Excellent alignment prevents pain and degenerative changes.

2. *Rest selectively!* Remember—rest is more than sleep. Use all types of rest to get its full benefits. Ask for help as needed.

3. *Relax intentionally!* Gently tuck your chin and pull your shoulders down toward your feet. Where are you holding tension? Put pressure on those tight areas and tighten those muscles. Feel the difference between the tense and relaxed state of the muscles. Use the color red to remind you to B-M-W and actively relax areas where you hold tension habitually.

4. *Massage gently!* Work on your head, neck, and ears. If you wear glasses, take them off and massage around your ears and temples. If you feel pain when you massage

your scalp or the base of your skull, use ice properly (as instructed later in the Train To Maintain section) and gently massage your scalp and the base of your neck until the pain ceases.

5. *Ice properly!* Use ice to stop muscle spasm and relieve pain (without causing frostbite).

Live It! For specific exercises:

Check out the Appendix:
Headaches to Plantar Fasciitis
Check out the Appendix:
Ice Therapy for Home Use

Access additional detailed instructions at 4x4Healing.com or check out the 4x4 Healing YouTube videos about caring for headaches, shoulder, back, knee pain, and more.

CHAPTER 18

The Challenges of Aging: Make the Most of Your Golden Years

Now that I am in my golden years, I relate better to the challenges of aging. People believe that young people are resistant to injury. However, the truth is that young bodies experience tissue micro-tears, strains, and sprains, just like old bodies. You heal faster when you are young.

Young or old, our bodies reflect the condition of our mind, emotions, and spirit. As you and I age, consider what we cannot change, but focus on improving. Grumbling and complaining waste time and foster bitterness, resentment, and anger. Use the tools presented in this book to deal with discomforts as they arise. Life is full of problems, pains, and joys. Strive to keep an attitude of gratitude without fear and worry about tomorrow. As you will see in the following chapters, building joy, forgiving offenses, and trusting our Creator establishes resiliency and coping strength through hard times.

Your attitude does not only impact your level of contentment—it also affects your internal chemistry. Bitterness, anger, resentment, and negative, sustained emotions elevate your adrenaline levels and your fight-flight-freeze reactions. Knowing and trusting in the true Living God provides coping capacity not available without Him. Experiencing your Creator's sufficiency and trustworthiness

> **Gratitude is a powerful antidote to depression.**

through life's joys and pains give you a foundation of internal peace, contentment, strength, endurance, and rest. How many times have you felt overwhelmed by crises, shattered dreams, and failed expectations? When you get to the end of your strength, where do you go?

When I went through my total knee surgeries about one year apart, I spoke to God about the pain that felt. It seemed too much to bear. I used ice regularly, which helped, but more than that, I prayed and remembered God's Word and promises, which provided deep comfort, endurance, and peace in the presence of the intense gnawing bone pain. Now, I gratefully thank God that He brought me through that pain. I am deeply grateful I no longer feel pain in my knees—work, yes, but not the previous nagging or intense pain.

Whether the challenges are physical pain, personal heartache, loss, or financial crisis, Jesus, my Creator provides my hope and strength. Through knowing Him—His character, His faithfulness, His almighty omniscience, omnipotence, and omnipresence—I trust Him to guide, provide, and get me through whatever comes my way. It is an amazing relief to be infused with rest, hope, joy, and deep peace that I could never experience without Him.

The following article, reprinted with the author's permission, beautifully exemplifies the way to face pain and death by faithfully trusting in God:

Pastor's Pen
"The Arms of Jesus"

As the cancer burst its bounds and began raging unchecked in her body, my wife mentioned to her niece that she was "ready to walk into the arms of Jesus." Some would dismiss such talk as empty religious jargon, but it is far from that. It is, in fact, rooted in historical reality. The Jesus she referred to is the conqueror of death. The Bible records three instances where Jesus interrupted funerals and raised the deceased to full life and vitality: Jairus' daughter, the son of the widow of Nain, and His friend, Lazarus. In each case the deceased was verifiably dead, not merely in a coma, and restored with no recuperation period. Then, to top that off, He Himself died in the most public way possible, spent three days in an airless tomb, and then emerged fully alive and appeared to over 500 eyewitnesses.

It would seem then that since death is an unavoidable reality for each of us, it would make sense that we would inquire about this phenomenal figure who mastered death and who promises that all who follow Him will live again. My wife was a Jesus-follower. She had committed her life to Jesus when she was sixteen and stayed close to Him the rest of her days.

Thus it was that when the specter of death loomed on her horizon, she would naturally look to this Jesus who passed through the portal of death, and who beckons to all who trust Him to come with Him through that same portal, not to annihilation or eternal suffering, but into the presence of the saints and angels and Jesus Himself. My wife died without fear, without anxiety, and without regret. That's how the friends of Jesus die. And that is why I am at peace in my soul. Who wouldn't want their beloved to be safe in the arms of Jesus?

Pastor Wayne

SECTION 4
TRAIN TO MAINTAIN

CHAPTER 19
Be Your Best: Don't Forget the Basics

Let's put it all together. The following list brings us back to the basics. Medication and medical advances are wonderful, but remember these foundational self-care basics:

- **Practice proper posture.** It is the foundation for function and health. Don't compromise! Be consistent! Use red dots or some other reminder throughout the day. Poor posture leads to headaches, compression fractures, back pain, and other painful problems.
- **Move it or lose it.** We either actively improve or passively decline. When you are sitting, it's essential to get up and walk around every 1-2 hours. During sleep at night, you will move around naturally. When awake, keep your feet dancing, B-M-W, and get up every two to three hours to prevent pressure sores, circulatory issues, and joint problems.
- **Use both sides of your body.** When you move one arm or leg, mimic the movement with the other arm or leg. Carry loads equally on each side. Stand evenly on both legs instead of lounging on one leg for prolonged periods. Use your legs reciprocally up and down the stairs to avoid weakening one side (which contributes to falls). When you are reaching—doing drywall work, cleaning the counter or shower, brushing your pet, or

painting the house—use your arms equally in all directions.

- **Exercise keeps your body, mind, circulation, nervous system, digestion, internal organ functions, and muscles performing effectively.** If you don't move, your body, joints, and muscles will hurt! Gentle, oscillating movements (B-M-W) will help joint lubrication, relieve stiffness and pain, and improve circulation.
- **Ask—don't force your body.** You can decrease your pain by working gently through it to regain strength and joint motion. The pain eventually goes away—but it will take consistency and time!
- **Grow old gracefully.** Age-related pain and problems can be as much in your mind as they are in your body. If you believe you can't do something, you probably can't. Take an honest appraisal of your condition related to your difficulties and desires. Get the opinion of trustworthy others. Maybe you can do more than you think. Instead of crossing off any possibility of improvement, ask, "How can I do this in a safe, healthy way?" or "How can I improve my strength or abilities?" Of course, the best approach to preventing pain and maintaining function is to keep dancing, walking, moving, and doing all that you can. For example, park your car a little farther away or take the stairs. Get wise counsel or professional help when you want more options.
- **Relieve pain effectively with ice.** It is wonderfully inexpensive and doesn't have the side effects of medication. Proper use of numbing cold increases circulation to help healing, decreases swelling, stops muscle spasm, and can speed structural improvement when used with corrective positions. The only caution is: Avoid frostbite!

 Check out the Appendix:
Ice Therapy for Home Use

- **Don't favor the weak or painful leg.** While it is a common reaction to weakness and poor alignment, leading with the strong leg when walking up and down steps causes the weak leg to become more vulnerable. Using only the strong leg also causes balance and structural problems. It is crucial to use both legs equally to regain strength. Use your arms to support your weight until you can rely solely on each leg's strength to hold your weight and slowly control each step.
- **Practice getting down and up from the floor daily.** This vital skill maintains strength and joint function in legs and arms, improves balance, and prevents falling. Getting up and down from hands and knees should be practiced daily. In the event of a fall, you'll need this ability. Whether you use sturdy furniture to stabilize your transfer or get down and up from the ground without aids, be safe! If you cannot get up and down from the ground safely, seek personal evaluation and training from a physical therapist.
- **Use your legs!** If you can stand at all, use your legs whenever possible to get stronger. Again, mental and physical safety first! If you can use your legs but use wheeled walkers and scooters, you accelerate leg, pelvis, and back weakness. Years ago, there were no wheeled walkers. Patients picked up standard walkers (without wheels or skis). Using a standard (pick-up) walker, you need to stop, gain and maintain your balance for a moment, use your trunk muscles to stand up straight, and rely on leg strength instead of arm strength to support your weight, one step at a time. Utilizing a pick-up walker, people gain back and leg strength and develop balance faster. They are then better able to graduate to a cane or no assistive device.

   When you lean heavily on your arms to push a wheeled walker instead of standing up straight to lift it, back pain and fall risk increase, and your balance is impaired. Stooped over, leaning heavily on your arms, you are heading for a fall.

Check out the Appendix:
Headaches to Plantar Fasciitis: Knees—Slow Sit Stand

- **Do what you can do**. Don't let others help you do what you can do yourself. To receive a courteous hand for safety is delightful, but don't let others pull you up. As much as possible, use your legs to do the work. Practice slow sit-to-stand throughout the day to build leg strength and alignment. The more you rely on others' strength or use your arms to lift or support you, the weaker your legs become.
- **Choose safety first!** Don't be afraid to ask for help when it's a matter of safety. When you ask, you bless the helper. If you are elderly, be thoughtful and considerate to your family by letting them know when you plan to do something potentially risky for you, e.g., walking alone, working in the garden, using a ladder or stool to reach overhead, or doing any new activity. Your family then knows to be present or to check on you periodically to ensure your safety.
- **Ask more of yourself, but don't force yourself!** When you exercise or participate in an activity, you may feel the temporary and manageable stretching or strengthening work. You will feel the discomfort of "work" and "good" pain but not "bad" pain. Progress gradually. If pain hinders you, stop the activity and seek professional advice.
- **Build quality before quantity.** Investing your energy in movement quality is more important than movement quantity. Be careful to do the activities as instructed. Stretch *actively* to protect the weak and vul-

nerable as you relax and lengthen the strong, tight areas. More is better only when done with the correct muscles in proper alignment and control.

Check out the Appendix:
Active Stretching

- **Scooters, electric lifts, or "launcher" chairs steal your strength**. The more you use a scooter or wheelchair when you can stand, the weaker your legs become. You must stand and walk to get on and off a scooter (which may trap you in a bathroom or other small spaces). Electric lifts or lift-chairs contribute to losing leg and trunk strength, diminishing balance, and decreasing hip and knee range of motion. Unless paralyzed, using motorized scooters and chairs will steal your leg and trunk strength and negatively impact your balance skills.

Key Points and Summary

- **Focus on your ability, potential, and motivation**. This book is for those who can make changes and have the potential and motivation to improve. If uncorrectable disabilities limit you, I admire your courage in working toward your potential. These general concepts are for your consideration. We will benefit if we persist in being the best we can be in body, mind, spirit, and attitude and seek help as needed.
- **Massage daily.** Wash and then massage tired, achy feet with moisturizing lotion after a long day of working to prevent numb or tingly feet and skin damage. Massage sore knees, arms, shoulders, head, and neck throughout the day. Stimulate your circulation with massage to help muscles relax. Remove your eyeglass-

es and massage around your ears, jaw, and base of your skull to prevent headaches and relieve neck and shoulder aches. If possible, find a good massage therapist to refresh your body periodically. Try to get a good massage every three months or more frequently to release tension and relax shoulder and back tissues you cannot reach. A good, deep massage that gets into the tissues (but does not make you tense) promotes good health and function.

- **Use Ice.** Proper numbing cold stops pain and muscle spasms. Follow the instructions and avoid frostbite!

 Check out the Appendix:
Ice Therapy for Home Use

- **Learn to Release.** Life is full of challenges and discomfort. Therefore, don't "what if" your way through tomorrow. The future is a mystery; the past is history. Don't let those concerns rob you of the gift of this moment—the present. Gratitude brings contentment and peace.
- **Deal with each ache, pain, frustration, and challenge as it happens.** Do what you can, then let it go. Don't let snapshot moments turn into life sentences. Practice keeping a hopeful attitude even during difficult times or when dealing with challenging people. Prevent external events from controlling you or negatively impacting your deep, internal peace, joy, and contentment.
- **Ask for help.** You are not alone. Support is available— look for it.
- **Forget the quick fix.** Lasting improvement requires commitment, training, practice, consistency, and time.
- **Value quality rest—it is critical and easily overlooked.** People seem not to know how to rest well, or

they rest too much. A still body, with an active mind or stirred emotions, is not at rest. When you are injured, you need restorative rest to give the body, mind, spirit, and emotions time to heal. If you want to stay healthy and active as you get older, balance your work and rest. Listen to your body. Be sure you experience high-quality recuperative rest.

- **Move it or lose it.** Ask your body to move fully and freely—don't force it. Instead, work toward normal motion and function.

  Two approaches in the American medical system:
  1. *You can't, so don't.* This approach sees a limitation and moves away from it, which results in dependence, increased limitation, and disability.
  2. *You can't, so let's find out why and correct it to your best potential.* This approach looks at your goals and abilities, your problems and potential, and moves toward your limitation, restoring and improving your condition and function.

- **Choose to improve, not settle**! Be proactive in improving your health and care. Ask questions. Understand why you received this advice. Search out other reasonable options. Be your best!

Personal Application

Review the information in the Let's Do This section and in the Appendix. Determine if these activities are easy for you to do well or if you have limitations. Make a list of problems and concerns. Track your symptoms and progress on a calendar. If you do not see the improvements you want, get professional help. A record of your status helps you see progress or regression—it also helps your professional providers discern multi-faceted origins and potential solutions for persisting problems.

Remember, this guide does not, in any way, replace a professional evaluation. Comprehensive evaluation and personalized treatment are always best to meet your individual needs and attain your goals. If you can make improvements on your own, without compensating (using the wrong muscles and positions), congratulations! If you find you are not making good quality progress or have questions or persistent discomforts, please seek professional help.

ঞ্চ ঞ্চ ঞ্চ ঞ্চ ঞ্চ

Our bodies express our deep emotions, harbored hurts, and beliefs. Physical treatment and training only provide temporary relief unless we address the non-physical causes of your symptoms. For comprehensive, lasting healing, correct physical problems while recognizing and replacing accepted lies with truth.

In the next section, we will discover how our minds impact our bodies, emotions, and lives.

PART THREE
YOUR MARVELOUS MIND

Don't let yesterday take up too much of today.
Will Rogers

Creativity is intelligence having fun.
Albert Einstein

Photo by Piotr Makowski on Unsplash

CHAPTER 20

Your Marvelous Mind

What we believe we live, whether we are aware of that fact or not. Your body expresses deeply held beliefs as well as your joys and pains. All of these impact your thoughts, choices, and life. Deep lies, harbored hurts, and painful encounters determine how you relate to people, your Creator, and your environment, just as safe joy-filled past experiences shape your core beliefs, perspectives, attitudes, and relationships. We can't change the past, but we can choose to improve the future. Understanding basic concepts about how your mind works helps heal past hurts and promote abundant life instead of settling and surviving. In a complex, hurting world, your amazing mind is resilient. The way you think and process information determines how you problem-solve, discern truth from lies, and make choices. Too many people suffer hopelessness and thus helplessness. Believing it's impossible to change, heal, and improve, people limit their potential, joy, and options and, instead, settle for the hand they have been dealt. Messages in your mind that say, "I have no options," or "I can't get better," or "Nothing will ever change," severely limit your health, joy, purpose, and full function.

Cultural Losses — Coping, Problem-Solving, and Identity

In recent years, American society increasingly relies on current trends to define our identity, condition, and potential. Personal value, perception of success, and acceptance seem dictated by how many "likes" you receive on Facebook, how many people you interact with on social media, and how accepted you feel via devices instead of face-to-face. People surrender their control of thought, problem-solving, self-awareness, responsibility, and distinctive identity to external forces like social media, group pressure, whimsical opinion, and misinformation.

This surrender of control allows society's fear, victimization, group affiliations, and rumors to erode your freedom, peace, and unique potential. Replacing self-awareness and self-regulation with external opinion and pressure promotes escalating fear, distorted perceptions, emotional reactivity, insecure identity, and poor coping skills. These trends aggravate the effects of past and current traumatic events, whether real or perceived.

Once people abdicate their responsibility for decision-making and self-care, they readily and without question, accept the information provided by social media, friends, the internet, and anyone with an opinion. This lack of curiosity, confirming facts, and discernment contributes to immature emotional reactions and misunderstanding.

How you see your identity plays a significant role in your overall health and function and how you see the world. When Doug received his diabetes diagnosis, he proactively participated in his care. Questioning the diagnosis and suggested treatment, he learned that the lab results and diagnosed condition was a passing snapshot in time, instead of a life sentence requiring unending medication and follow-up appointments.

Will you settle for what others think and choose for you? Don't lose your voice or your choice!

Dangerous Expectations

As noted before, our culture naturally gravitates to instant gratification, quick fix, and entitlement mentality. This self-centered inclination focuses on what we don't have instead of gratitude for what we do have. Social media magnifies general and superficial comparisons, leading to envy, greed, resentment, and blame. Bitterness, anger, depression, and victimization feelings result from unrealistic hopes and dreams, false expectations, or inaccurate beliefs. Examine these dangerous expectations (lies) that could affect your health:

- "Healthy" or "normal" means I should not experience pain
- I am solely responsible for protecting myself and my loved ones from all harm
- If I do all the right things, I will not have diseases, pain, or health problems
- I'm a good person, and if I do all the right things, I will be in heaven forever.
- I deserve what others have—status, possessions, marriage, children, etc.
- Life should be fair (whatever that means)
- Material comforts guarantee my happiness
- Bad things shouldn't happen to good people
- God can't or won't help me—I've done too many bad things
- Morals, ethics, and character don't matter—the end justifies the means
- What I do or choose won't affect anyone else

Dangerous expectations lead to discontent, a self-centered outlook, loss, blame, entitlement, and resentment. Festering negative feelings produce chronic stress and cortisol production that can increase disease processes.

SECTION 1

DO YOU KNOW

CHAPTER 21

Trauma Effects on Development: You Can Reclaim Losses

Healthy childhood development results from safe, consistent, verbal and nonverbal human interaction. Joy-filled nurturing establishes a child's secure identity, teaches healthy coping skills, and builds return-to-joy ability and strength. Joy is a potent motivator from birth and is the fuel for positive stress management.[12]

Childhood trauma creates gaps and delays in healthy mental, emotional, and relational development. People living in chaos, growing up with constant turmoil, abuse, and mixed messages, have a much lower tolerance for real or perceived adversity.[13]

Childhood abuse and neglect often result in physical, emotional, relational, or mental problems in adulthood. Prolonged stresses and persistent defensive reactions can cause chronic physical pain, excessive fatigue, immune 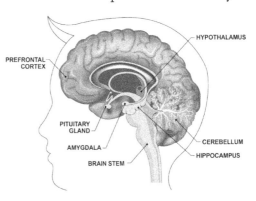 system dysfunction, functional issues, and negative thought and choice behaviors. Brain imaging studies confirm the relationship between chronic pain and changes in the brain caused by trauma. Brain scans of prolonged abuse and trauma survivors show that the right orbital prefrontal cortex (ROPC) shrinks, and serotonin receptors are destroyed. We see consistent patterns of accelerated brain degeneration in the brain scans of patients with chronic pain.[14]

The good news is the brain can be healed and restored.

Healthy humans need person-to-person, face-to-face communication, and contact. During every interpersonal interaction, both hemispheres of your brain communicate simultaneously but differently. While the left hemisphere controls linguistic communication and analytical interpretation, the right hemisphere manages emotional and nonverbal communications.

Check out the Appendix:
Are Your Words Heard?

Sensory information—stimulus received through touch, smell, sight, sound, and taste—travel quickly to the brain's thalamus. Those processed sensations answer the question, "What is happening to me?" From the thalamus, the organized impressions go in two directions:

1. To the *amygdala*, deep in the limbic system, where processing occurs instantly without our conscious awareness. There the conditions are determined to be threatening or non-threatening.
2. To the *logic centers* in the frontal lobes of the brain at a slower speed for conscious processing.

Both brain hemispheres work together to seek and verify the incoming information's consistency and accuracy, filtered through experience and emotional overlay.

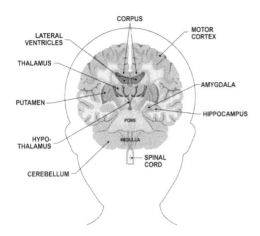

The conclusion, message, and meaning your brain accepts may or may not be accurate. Our interpretation of daily events filters through past experiences, pains, joys, beliefs, and might be correct or erroneous.

Early traumatic experiences alter brain function and cause conflicting interpretations of sensory and cognitive input. These emotional, nonverbal messages are the most powerful. If the traumatic error messages remain unhealed, powerful emotional beliefs from childhood trauma and neglect can last into adulthood. Dominant survival perceptions override cognitive reason, reinforce threat messages, affect relationships, and impact mental and physical health. Long-term effects of living in constant survival mode negatively impact the brain and sympathetic nervous system. Persistent fear or feeling unsafe (whether perceived or real) devastates every aspect of health. But the good news is the brain can be healed and restored. Truth replaces embedded lies. Harbored hurts and deep wounds can heal.

When trauma occurs in adulthood, recovery depends on how much truth and health the person experienced before the trauma. Combat soldiers, law enforcement, and others who repeatedly deal with death threats within a law-abiding, moral framework and do not suffer PTSD have a foundation of purpose—such as protecting innocents or stopping evil— and have a healthy sense of identity. If these public servants must use lethal force to protect, they will need time to recover from trauma involving death, but they will heal. The trauma does not persist.

A person may not be conscious of past abuse and trauma until adulthood due to dissociation, amnesia, or survival reactions at the time of the incident. When overwhelmed, the brain can block out harrowing memories and confuse messages for a while until the individual is ready and mature enough to heal those deep invisible wounds.

During this deep healing, it is vital to avoid reliving past traumatic events. When ready, and with caring support, the survivor can report safely as a distant observer to process memories.

If you experienced life-changing trauma, you might be afraid of healing for many reasons. You may settle for living with residual pain and limitation. But, if you want to experience the incomparable joy and blessing of being whole, free, and healed, survivors confirm the benefits of their healing journey are worth the challenge. And you don't need to do this alone.

CHAPTER 22

Strengthening Your ROPC Through Joy: You Can Build JOY!

From infancy, humans mirror messages they receive non-verbally. Face-to-face communication between two people is simultaneously active on emotional, cognitive, and verbal levels.

The right orbital prefrontal cortex (ROPC) is believed to be the human brain's major joy center. Your ROPC develops significantly between birth and eighteen months of age. Brain scans confirm that feelings of joy generated through eye contact and smiling faces communicating, "I am happy to see you," "I am happy to be with you," and "You are valued and accepted for who you are," cause growth in the ROPC. A child less than one-year-old actively seeks and is motivated by this sensation of joy.

A child's brain synchronizes with the more mature person's emotions, even mimicking the mentor's brain chemistry.

Immature brains grow in proportion to the amount of exposure to a more mature brain.[15]

Mature Brain vs. Immature Brain

Infants operate only on emotion, but as we mature, gain experience, and grow in cognitive reasoning, we balance emotional impulses with facts and understanding. Emotional influence creates powerful and long-lasting impressions. Whether true or not, the emotions we feel through life experiences determine the messages and perceptions attached to those experiences.

> How much and how fast the joy center of your brain grows depends directly on the nature and quality of healthy stimulation that you receive through interaction with a healthy, more mature brain.

A mature brain processes sensory and intellectual information in a way that consistently agrees with reality. It:

- Reconciles and balances emotional and cognitive impulses. The meaning generated from the incoming stimulus, whether threatening or non-threatening, is clear and makes sense.
- Develops options, makes the best choice, and takes action toward a clear goal.
- Matches emotional, verbal, and body language appropriate to the interaction and the situation.

Immature child brains have insufficient truth, joy, and healthy relationship experience to arrive at clear, accurate, realistic meanings for uncomfortable experiences. The immature brain seeks the harmony and order of a mature brain.

Joy or Happiness? There is a difference

In the English language, we often use happiness and joy interchangeably, but I want to differentiate the two in quality and source. Happiness, defined here, is the temporary emotion that occurs in response to pleasant, enjoyable events, circumstances, or activities.

In contrast, consider joy—an enduring state of deep, internal, spiritual contentment, peace, and ethereal delight beyond external influences, circumstances, or description. The only Source of joy is our Creator. In close connection with Him, joy also has the qualities of:

1) *Identity*—knowing the awe-inspiring attributes of our Creator and knowing your own God-given identity,
2) Profound *trust* in love, wisdom, power, protection, provision, and confidence in His ability beyond yourself
3) *Hope* in the promises of our trustworthy Creator.

Happiness comes and goes with changing events, but joy stays with you through troubles and triumphs, hurts and happiness. Joy feeds your ROPC, which gives you tenacity and strength through difficult, stressful times.

Recreation, laughter, and playful fun build happiness and a sense of joy (identity and value—"I am happy to be with you"), which restores brain and body health, increases competitive endurance, builds coping resiliency, decreases fatigue, and prevents depression.

Trauma Effects on the ROPC

Trauma creates an obstacle to normal development. Brain imaging of trauma, abuse, and neglect survivors show significant atrophy (wasting or decreased size of tissue) and a lower number of

Joy center deficits can be restored in persons suffering previous developmental or trauma losses.

ROPC cells.[16] Traumatized young brains bombarded by mixed signals, inconsistent verbal and nonverbal communication, and overwhelming experiences cannot accurately process safety, personal identity and control, or rational meaning from life events.

Depressed, angry, or wounded adult brains pass on negative perceptions, attitudes, and relational confusion to the young brain. Therefore, immature and traumatized brains are vulnerable to distorted sensory messages.

Hurt people hurt people. But your joy center (ROPC) can grow and be restored through safe joy-building experiences and accepting sincere messages of personal value.

ROPC Can Regenerate

The ROPC grows with gradual, healthy, safe, joyful stimulus, and atrophies (shrinks) with neglect, trauma, abuse, or persistent mixed messages. When your facial, body, and verbal communication is synchronous, consistent, and appropriate in every emotion you feel, your mature brain passes on positive, secure, healthy identity, and coping ability to more immature or wounded brains.

Just as a child's brain grows and matures, so can adult brains because the joy center (mainly considered the right orbital prefrontal cortex—ROPC) of the brain can regenerate.

SECTION 2
FOOD FOR THOUGHT

CHAPTER 23

What We Believe Is What We Live: Don't be Deceived

There are three main questions that our brains want answered:

1. Do others value me?
2. What is happening to me?
3. What does this experience say about my identity?[17]

Our answers to these questions determine what we believe about who we are, our Creator, other people, our purpose, our potential, and the meaning of life events. Let's look at how our brains process information to answer these questions.

Are Others Happy To Be With Me?

We are social beings. It is healthy to show relational pleasure at being together. Our ROPC is stimulated and grows in the presence of face-to-face eye contact, smiles, and voice tones that radiate acceptance and joy at being together. Knowing we are highly valued establishes a secure identity, increases confidence, and develops coping skills. Knowing that other people love us enough to correct us is probably more important than showing social acceptance. Consistent love, respect, and approval must accompany messages of displeasure for correction. But past trauma can turn loving correction—for the good of that person—into perceived shame and punishment.

With a history of drug abuse, addictions, and abusive or manipulative social connections, messages and gestures of true love, correction, and care are received as condemnation. The actual meaning of deep concern and correction are distorted by "pain-colored glasses." This distortion makes the hope of healing and reconciliation with loved ones difficult.

Our son struggled for twenty years with his destructive life choices. Finally, he had enough and sought support and healing. Though the consequences of his bad decisions felt overwhelming, he decided to heal deep emotional wounds and change his life, return to family encouragement, and accept loving accountability. He affirms that God saved his life through our prayers, patience, tough love, and healthy boundaries. He knows he is extremely loved and valued. Joy, peace, and confidence replaced his discouragement, anxiety, shame, and insecurity.

What Is Happening To Me?

Sensation messages travel at high-speed from the thalamus to the amygdala. If danger is perceived, the amygdala activates your fight-flight-freeze reactions before your conscious brain evaluates the situation.

Have you ever had someone scare you, and you ran away before you realized there was no real threat? Accurately understanding what is happening to you depends on reconciling the immediate emotional and threat reactions with your brain's slower logical processing.

What Does This Experience Say About Me?

Unhealthy interactions—abuse, neglect, mixed messages, persistent harsh tone of voice, or facial expressions indicating displeasure, anger, or rejection—negatively affect the brain's joy center. In the immature or wounded brain, these instill error messages such as "I am not important," "Something is wrong with me," or the other person's reaction or choice "is my fault."

Appropriate displeasure signals received and understood to be corrective—out of love for you and your benefit—do not starve your joy center. Consistent experiences of safety, value, and loving correction build joy, strength, and the ability to cope with challenges. Loving correction establishes joy, trust, true identity, and value.

Question Your Fears

We receive emotional messages every day. Well-established rational assessment skills balance initial emotional reactions resulting in an accurate understanding and response. Fear messages prevalent in our society activate adverse reactions. We self-limit and reject joy experiences by reacting to perceptions of fear that pose no threat.[18]

In the early 1950s, a happy two-year-old girl was diagnosed with polio. Her shocked parents agonized as they watched her from behind a glass barrier for weeks on end. They knew the statistics and stories—children in iron lungs, too many deaths—but they fought the fear and trusted God.

I was that little girl. The doctors warned about the post-polio syndrome, but I've not experienced any of the predicted maladies. Instead, I choose to reject the fear and approach life with a positive attitude.

While unpreventable diseases and disabilities limit us, we have a choice to savor life and deal with problems as they come, instead of living fearfully. When we make this choice, we experience more joy, full function, and improved health of body, mind, and soul.

Don't be a victim. You are valuable, unique, and you have God-given purpose.

Be victorious!

CHAPTER 24

Your Thoughts Are Showing: How Are Your Values Revealed?

Each day, thousands of messages bombard you from outside sources and from inside your head. The external communications bring endless decision-making opportunities. Though credited to many sources, this principle remains accurate: Watch your thoughts for they become words. Watch your words for they become actions. Watch your actions for they become habits. Watch your habits for they become your character. And watch your character for it becomes your destiny. What we think, we become.

While I agree, let's add: Watch your thoughts and words because they become choices, and choices become actions. According to Psychology Today's blog, "the average person makes an eye-popping 35,000 choices per day. Assuming most people spend around seven hours per day sleeping and thus blissfully choice-free, that makes roughly 2,000 decisions per hour, or one decision every two seconds."[19] Through daily sorting and decision-making, you consciously and subconsciously accept and reject information and actions. Ask yourself these three questions:

1. Will I be influenced by and agree with what is said?
2. Will I decide the information is worth considering later?
3. Will I recognize the information as junk and delete the thought, choice, or action?

That process of responding, storing, or deleting information and messages continues each day. The words we say and replay in our minds affect how we see ourselves, the world, other people, our Creator, and how we make decisions.

Our Creator designed and created everything through the power of His Word. Yet, we pay little attention to the self-talk that influences our choices. Our thoughts become internal messages which become beliefs and attitudes that shape our perspectives, decisions, and actions. These create a feedback loop through a small area of the brain that acts as a filter—the reticular activating system (RAS).

As thousands of sight, sound, touch, and taste sensations barrage you every day, your RAS filter focuses on and gathers whatever supports your desires. If you imagine you want a puppy, your RAS filter draws your attention to everything puppy related. You notice puppies everywhere—not kittens, horses, fish, or birds. Decide you want a German Shepherd puppy? Suddenly, that's all you see. Your RAS filter spotlights your desires and expectations. This focusing loop can lead you into a depressing downward spiral of lies, discouragement, and failed expectations or energize and propel you to achieve lofty goals.

Look at this illustration. Notice how every element of the circle impacts the others. You could connect many zigzagging arrows inside it:

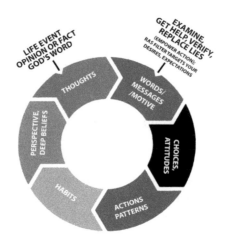

1. Thoughts produce words that get organized into meaning and messages. These messages gel into motives, desires, and speech. Your RAS filter gathers information (true or false, good or bad) to reinforce your desires and expectations.
2. Experience fused with desires and motives produce attitudes and determine choices.
3. Attitudes fuel your impulsive, emotional reactions, or your discerning, well-considered plans for action.
4. Actions become patterns and habits that feed positive or negative perspectives, strengthened by resulting consequences or rewards.
5. Your perspectives establish your belief system about the world, other people, yourself, and your Creator.
6. Your deep beliefs are the solid or faulty foundation of your thoughts—and the cycle continues.

What we believe is what we live. We are dynamic beings—we either passively get worse or actively get better. Without examination and correction, the cycle of lie messages, wounds, and poor life choices continues to drag us down into a destructive pattern of thoughts, statements, and deeds. On the other hand, with examination and healthy support, a positive truth-based cycle strengthens and promotes our health, growth, maturity, function, and relationships.

Check out the Appendix:
Reticular Activating System (RAS)

Change Your Thoughts to Release Your Pain

Wounds received from child abuse or another mistreatment rightly result in anger, grief, and other strong emotions. Additionally, you may harbor deep beliefs like "No one cares," "I am worthless," and "My life can never get better." Frequently in adulthood, these wounds and emotions surface, but you can temper powerful emotions with understanding and forgiveness. Forgiving does not mean forgetting or condoning the injury. But it does provide perspective for healing and putting the pain in the past. Forgiving frees the hurting person of haunting anger, bitterness, and desire for revenge. Forgiving transfers the responsibility of the event to the perpetrator and God's judgment.

Our Creator will judge abuse and injury, especially toward children and the helpless. People who honor God—who hate what He hates and love what He loves—feel righteous rage against evil intentions and actions.

What you believe can cause potent physical reactions. In a society inundated with fear messages, threats, perceived loss of control, and victim mentality, people experience a disruption to their daily activity or sleep. Sudden symptoms include a racing heart, profuse perspiration, or pain in shoulders, back, abdomen, or chest. These unexpected symptoms can be terrifying and naturally increase stress and initiate the Fear-Pain-Tension Cycle.

When you experience these sudden physical responses, remember to B-M-W.

When you quiet those initial reactions, you interrupt the Fear-Pain-Tension Cycle and allow your emotional and mental functions to stabilize. Care with a counselor, pastor, or 4X4 Healing Trail Guide will help you examine your deep beliefs, discover the truth, and replace stress and worry with plan and purpose.

For more information on individual 4x4 Healing care, check out my website: 4x4Healing.com

Psalm 46:10 begins, "Be still and know that I am God." "Being still" is not impatient, finger-drumming, time-wasting, habitual fretting over rumor or opinion. Your choice to respond to God's call to "Be still" means to "stop striving," to calm your physical reactions, so you think clearly, assess your internal stresses, and trust Him—all elements of an obedient, personally satisfying, healthy habit.

Through examination and self-awareness, you can change your thoughts and beliefs. Essentially, what we feed on, we express. If we spend our time around bitter, hurtful, grumbling, complaining, easily offended people who see themselves as victims, we pick up those tendencies. Conversely, if we seek nurturing, grateful, forgiving people who take personal responsibility and see themselves as victors, life's pain and problems become opportunities to conquer with time, determination, and support.

Your thoughts impact the people around you. Since your body language, vocal tone, and facial expression send a more dominant message than your words, misunderstanding can happen quickly. It is good to consider that the response I receive contains my message's meaning.

> I know you believe you understand what you think I said, but I am not sure you realize that what you heard is not what I meant.
> — ROBERT MCCLOSKEY

Clear communication depends on the sender being self-aware enough to recognize her internal hurts, perspectives, and reactions in the verbal and nonverbal messages. The speaker also must be sensitive and aware of how others receive the intended message. Clinicians, parents, and everyone in a mentor relationship need to have healthy self-awareness. If this seems difficult, I am right there with you—I work at this constantly. So, let's do this together:

- As the sender or speaker, observe the receiver and tune into her nonverbal responses. Listen carefully to the recipient's reactions and tone of voice to confirm whether your intended message was accepted. Make your best effort to send clear, concise, accurate messages tailored to the receiver's age, emotional state, and comprehension level.

- As a listener and receiver, pay attention and listen carefully. Stay with the speaker. Don't let your thoughts run ahead or interrupt. If what you hear seems confusing or inconsistent with what you know of the person or the topic, ask for clarification. You can avoid so much conflict, misunderstanding, and hurt feelings when you listen carefully and clarify confusion or inconsistencies before concluding the conversation. I feel a deeper heart-to-heart connection when I listen well.

CHAPTER 25

What Messages Do You Accept?
You Decide Whom You Follow

Messages from our desires, concerns, emotions, conscience, and physical body course through our brains along with thousands of external messages each day. Even before we open our eyes when waking, our sensory systems send us input—some we ignore, and some we accept and take action.

While sleeping, you may not remember or react to a dream, but you will probably adjust if you are too warm or too cold. Whether external or internal, verbal or nonverbal, your mind's accepted messages affect every part of life.

Advertising messages blast from devices all around you. They tell you that you are not content, not happy, not accepted unless you buy or do what they say. Sometimes you respond, and other times you reject the message. Accustomed to this flow of persuasion, you rarely stop to think about the motive behind the suggestion or where the message originated. Often, you react based on your beliefs, habitual decision making, or fatigue level.

The Four Voices

Mental messages come from four primary sources:

1. The world's systems and values
2. The flesh's desires and self-will

3. Satan—the enemy of the Triune God and His people
4. The One True Creator God—Father, Son, and Holy Spirit

> We have one mouth and two ears—a good indicator we should listen more than we speak.

The world voice prioritizes external looks, performance, money, power, and messages like "You should do, be, or look like ___ to be accepted," "Success is getting ahead no matter what it takes," "The one with the most toys wins," etc.

Flesh messages come from pride and self-focus—my will, my way, my need, my defense, my desire, my agenda, etc. Flesh ideas include phrases like, "Me first," "I can do it myself," "I don't need God or other people," "I know this is wrong, but I want it," "It's okay as long as I don't get caught," "I need what you have more than you do," or "If I can keep this secret, it won't hurt anyone else." In the long run, these lies backfire.

The third and fourth voices also have personality. Though they are from the spiritual realm, they are real and powerful. Who is the Source of good, moral, ethical, and merciful thought and action? Who is the source of pride, wickedness, and deceit?

I believe we live in a spiritual realm as well as a physical, tangible world. Therefore, I believe there is a powerful enemy of the Creator Jesus and His people. This powerful spiritual being (also created by the One True God) chose to defy and oppose his Maker (see Isaiah 14:12-16 and the book of Job, especially Chapter 1). Satan (which means "adversary") was a beautiful creation of God who chose his evil path. He is not more powerful or equal in any way to Creator God, but he can invade our minds with his influence—if we let him.

We hear Satan's voice (the third source) in our thoughts. His voice accuses, demeans, and slanders people and the character of God. The enemy's messages are thoughts like "You are bad," "You've done too much wrong—you are too far gone," "God will not and cannot forgive and restore you," "No one cares for you," "You are all alone," "You don't deserve anything good," and "Your Creator does not care for you or love you." Those statements are lies. Satan is the father of lies and deception.[20] Satan seeks to deceive and mislead those who honor our Creator.

The fourth voice belongs to our Creator God who speaks words of forgiveness, patience, kindness, encouragement, guidance, and unconditional love. Jesus died for all people—the perfect Lamb of God—for our mistakes and disobedience. We need a Savior.[21] Those who feel they don't need help cannot receive Jesus' gift of life and debt payment because they refuse Him. Only those who recognize they need help, turn from selfishness and wickedness, ask Jesus to forgive and save them, receive forgiveness, and enter into a new life.

We are in the midst of a raging spiritual battle for control of our minds and hearts. There are only two eternal destinies— which side will you be on? Satan and God are not equal in power. Think of the difference between God and Satan like this: Jesus is like the oceans of the world. Satan, the created fallen angel, is like a teaspoon of acid. No comparison.

Satan is a powerful spiritual being who is totally under the control of Creator God. In his insane pride, Satan wants to be equal to or greater than God so he is warring against Almighty God and His people. Our Creator wants relationship with people who chose to love and honor Him. Genuine love demands the freedom to choose.

Satan tries to lure people away from knowing and pleasing God through deception and temptation. He uses his own voice of accusation and lies to entice hearts and minds away from truth and relationship with God. Satan uses the voices and allure of the flesh—the my-way-highway of self-focus and pride—and the world voice of materialism, performance, and man's opinion to manipulate and distort your values. That's the small but powerful "acid" that can burn you. But if you submerge in the vast expanse of the sea (Creator Jesus), the acid (the enemy of God and His people, Satan) is overpowered and vanquished. Which voice do you follow? There are only two eternal destinies and only one voice leads you to eternal peace, joy, and relationship with your Creator. Which do you choose?

SECTION 3
LET'S DO THIS!

CHAPTER 26

Living in the Snap: There is Hope in Your Darkest Hour

Your mind affects your overall health. The way you think and manage stress originates from your motives, internal soul hunger, deep wounds, and unmet needs.[22] Think of any situation that felt impossible, but you were able to get through it. Hopelessness can lead to depression and suicide. But there is always hope if you look for it. *Hopefulness* invigorates endurance, persistence, and problem-solving. Aware of them or not, your resiliency and perseverance are strongly influenced by experience and present mental attitude.

One way to tap into hopefulness involves living in the snap. When you face an overwhelming situation, remember previous times where God pulled you through. One moment all seems hopeless. But suddenly, the solution appears, and the problem disappears—"The Snap."

Our family has experienced financial, health, and hope crises that have turned from daunting to done—when the need is met—in an instant.

Don't credit coincidence. Respond to answered prayer—snap moments—with gratitude to our Creator. Remember previous calamities that God brought you through in a "snap." God is faithful. Read His Word to know Him and His promises. Trust Him beyond your understanding and share your heart with Him, as David did in the Psalms.

CHAPTER 27

O-C-A — Options-Choice-Action: Consider All Your Possibilities

How many choices do you have if you believe there are no options? If you thought, "Zero!" you are correct.

When you feel trapped, victimized, and helpless, you can't see possible options for improvement. Enduring trauma at an early age hinders development and results in "black and white, all or nothing" thinking. Healthy experience and training are needed to see the vast spectrum of options available between two extremes.

A practical tool I teach is O-C-A: Options-Choice-Action. You need to know your **Options** before you can make a **Choice**. If you cannot see a wide range of Options, you need to learn how to recognize more possibilities, discern positive and negative outcomes, and then make a wise Choice. The steps to realistic healthy problem-solving must be discovered and practiced. Once you recognize the broad variety of good and bad Options, you have the opportunity to learn how to make the best Choice. Then, the hardest or possibly the scariest part of O-C-A is to **Act** on that best Choice.

People who experienced past trauma may only see extreme all-or-nothing solutions to their problems. Unless they have a chance to expand their imagination, experience, and perspective with the guidance of a healthy caregiver, they may not see the extensive scope of possibilities between their familiar "run or succumb" options.

Many of the childhood trauma survivors I work with have difficulty coming to the office for the first time. They report they want to run away before they ever start their healing journey. As we work together and build trust, they confide they were afraid they had only two choices: "be trapped and controlled" or "run away." But they found that their perceptions were wrong—they found unimaginable joy, freedom, empowerment, and healing by taking that first scary step. Prolonged childhood experience of *having little or no choice and no voice* persists into adult life.

Education expands the scope of possibilities, and jump-starts suppressed imagination. Positive, safe experiences fortify the reality of varied options and opportunities.

> **What you believe determines the choices you make and the life you lead.**

Training Your Mind

Remember, what you believe determines the choices you make and the life you lead. As Henry Ford said: "Whether you think you can, or you think you can't–you're right." With focused goals, you will most likely take the necessary steps and make progress toward them. Self-limiting and God-limiting messages destroy your joy, rob your potential, and cause you to survive, not to thrive in life.

Opinions come at you from every direction. Do you question the opinions and diagnoses you receive? Look for evidence, ask questions, and don't let a *snapshot in time* become a life sentence.

When you face a crisis, do you struggle and find yourself tempted to give up, or do you get help to discover more options? When that happened to Joni Eareckson Tada, founder of JoniandFriends.org, she overcame a life-shattering spinal cord injury from a diving accident. Today, she lives a life full of purpose, talent, and ministry.[23]

Frequently my patients experience improvement and diagnosis reversals when they consider multiple options. Our daughter struggled with animal allergies. Putting into practice my education and experience, we sought healing. Here's how she describes her journey:

> *"I struggled off and on with some animal allergies since I was a little girl. However, my mom refused to let that become part of my identity or be a limitation in my life. Mom taught me that you don't need all the details or know what causes every symptom. Be open to the idea that you might not have to live with it permanently, nor is it your identity. When I liberated my thinking to accept that what I feel is not part of who I am or how I have to live, suddenly everything became manageable, treatable, and curable.*
>
> *Now I live with a cat and a rabbit. I can be around all kinds of animals with no allergy problems. Sure, there are occasions where I sneeze or get a little itchy, but that could be dust in my eyes or up my nose, which a tissue, washcloth, or eyewash remove. It is a normal reaction for anyone in a dusty or hairy environment. Allergies have no place in my life. My mom is right. There's no reason people should be allergic to natural things like food or animals.*
>
> *Chemicals may be a different story, but nature is nature. It is part of our lives from birth. I have confidence that if there is a perceived allergy to something natural like food or animals, such an allergy can be cured and does not have to rob you of joy or be a limitation.*
>
> *I love my mom's no contracts attitude in response to medical issues. This attitude allows God to do miracles. Contracts refer to those messages we accept and believe about ourselves. When I say, 'I can't be around cats,' or 'I can't _____,' then I put a contract on myself to permanently live that way because of my belief. I prevent any possibility of ever being free of those limitations.*

Instead, I seek to correct the current, temporary problem and give my body the tender loving care it needs until I return to the activities I enjoy.

My mother deals with each symptom and diagnosis on a case by case basis and does not blanket them with a universal limitation. Instead, she trains the mind and body to maximize total health, minimize weaknesses, and be the best you can be. Her approach is extremely rare and beautiful in the medical field!"

Victim or Victor?

The decision is yours. Life comprises one situation, one circumstance, one problem after another—each one comes with choices. You actively improve or passively deteriorate.

> **It is important to retrain the mind and body during any healing process.**

This book encourages you to ask, verify, and learn as many options as possible so you can make optimal decisions and be the best you can be. Think about these questions:

1. What does it mean to make the best of your situation or to be your best?
2. Do you fear challenges or see them as problem-solving opportunities?
3. Do you depend on your abilities to conquer troubles, or do you ask and trust your Creator?
4. Are you able to tackle a problem and break it down into steps to correct or improve it?
5. Do you correct small discomforts as soon as they start or wait for intense pain?

Consider modifying your thinking to continually ask, "What could be better" to improve your life and the lives of those around you. Become aware of options and changes that smooth and strengthen life. Grow in awareness of your body and your feelings. Practice healthy possibilities you never considered before.

When you recognize more options, you increase your creative thinking and problem-solving skills. Your sensitivity to improving your comfort and condition translates into an increased awareness of how others feel. Now, you can help others experience more safety and comfort.

Practice O-C-A (Options-Choice-Action) on small decisions as well as big ones. Tiny irritations provide opportunities to creatively evaluate possible improvements, replace bad habits with healthy ones, and avoid the exhausting drama that magnifies frustration and the problem. The way you handle little issuess sets your default for handling big problems.

Check out the Appendix:
Reactive   or   Responsive Decision-Making Steps

Sort the good from the bad, then prioritize your options. Assess the immediate and long-term benefits and detriments of your good options—for you and others involved. With the information you have, make the choice that leads to the best result. As with any skill, you become more proficient and comfortable with practice.

Are you ready to practice these principles?

Live It! Living in the Snap

Think back to an overwhelming situation. How did you get through it? What were your thoughts and feelings in the crisis?

- Write down a seemingly impossible crisis that turned out well.

- Write down what helped you get through the trial—prayer, counting your blessings, support of friends and family, relaxation, exercise, peaceful worship music, conversation, counsel, etc.
- In future trials, what will help you manage stress? Make a list of what helps you live in the snap every day, especially through difficult times. Living in the snap means you gratefully focus on future hope and God's unseen possibilities beyond human strength, understanding, or control. You choose to trust how God works out your impossible situation and be content with the result.
- Think about what causes you to worry. Is it enough money for gas, coffee, lunch, a bill, house payment, or another need? How has God provided? Maybe you worry about a sneeze or cough, but you do not get sick. Perhaps you had a serious disease but were healed. When you experience pain, are you grateful when the pain ceases?
- Make a list of the little and big things for which you are grateful. Our Creator showers us with His mercy every day—the sun, air, physical and mental abilities, pain relief, food, shelter, wisdom to solve a problem or resolve a conflict, and more.

Live It! Managing Expectations

Take a moment to search the messages running through your mind. Make a list of dangerous expectation messages that focus on what you do not have or things that have not turned out the way you want.

Choose the item on your list that causes you the most pain or haunts your thoughts. Write down your thoughts, words, and feelings about this issue. With support from an insightful, caring friend, look over what you have written to find the core of this pain. Ask God to show you what you need to heal the pain. Write down any lies or wounds that feed this pain.

How can you manage or change your pain, your condition? What can you not control or influence? List how you will replace lies and failed dreams with truth and hopeful goals. Write down how you will change victim and envy messages in your thoughts to grateful, content messages. When negative thoughts enter your mind, immediately counter those thoughts with the positive ideas you have listed. Turn your inward hurt into outward gratitude. Reflect on and proclaim your blessings out loud.

Live It! Practice Truthful Positive Talk

Healthy self-talk is not just wishful thinking. Winning self-talk proclaims *truthful* messages about yourself, God, the situation, and your potential:

- Be aware of negative messages in your head. Write down any negative, self-limiting, condemning statements.
- List your past successes and how you have seen God work in your life. Write down positive truths about yourself—big and small—such as: You try new things, you desire to do well, and you want better health, life, and relationships.
- Replace the automatic negative replay in your mind with the positive truth statements. Practice this daily. Have these truth statements readily accessible. Train your brain to reflect on positive truths, victories, and future hopes instead of past limitations and losses. Look forward, not backward, throughout your day.

Live It! Identify the Source and Recognize the Voice

The best way to decrease mental stress is to recognize the messages in your mind. Choose which ones you want to follow and which ones to delete.

- Make a list of the messages that circulate through your mind.
- Go through the list and write which voice each message comes from: 1) your flesh or your will, 2) the world—human opinion, the shoulds of this world, 3) the accuser, the enemy of God and His people (Satan), 4) God, your Creator, who made you and has great plans for you.[24]
- Look at your list. What voice is most prevalent? Is that the voice you want to have in your mind to guide your choices and your life?
  o Change the undesirable. Replace negative, lie messages with truth messages from God—He made you, He knows you, and you are so precious to Him!
  o Reinforce the positive. Repeat truth messages from the Source.
- Refuse unwanted statements. Whenever the negative messages come into your mind, reject the unwanted statement out loud and replace it by declaring true, positive messages out loud. Writing the negative and positive messages helps you recognize, refuse, and replace quickly and trains your thinking. Speaking out loud as you reject the negative and replace it with the positive reinforces healing in your mind, heart, body, and spirit.
- Live out the positive truth message. Find help and loving accountability to rewrite your mental software and exercise your new choices.

Live It! Be Your Best!

Picture yourself in a hospital, doctor's, dentist's, or physical therapist's office to receive the care you need.

- Remember why you came to the clinic or hospital. What benefit do you gain by going through this procedure? Hold tightly to the good reason for being there and the desired outcome.

- If you feel uncomfortable, B-M-W while you are in the facility. Remember the good reasons you made this choice.
- Prepare for your medical examination or procedure. While you undress and get into a gown, listen to your body and feelings.
- Write down your feelings and the messages associated with those feelings.
- You are in your private room, waiting for your health care provider. What would make you feel better? Would it be nice to have a blanket to wrap around yourself until the clinician arrived? What keeps you from asking for a cold bottle of water, a comfortable place to sit, some soft music, or slipper socks to keep your feet warm?

> **Remember that you can say "stop" anytime. Use reminders to B-M-W, take a break, get a drink or a blanket, call a friend, ask for help, etc.**

- You can bring comfort items with you or ask the staff to improve your comfort.
- Tell your health care professional that you will say "stop" when you are uncomfortable or have questions. It will be challenging to interrupt some procedures, so prepare your caregiver for your need to say "stop." Help your caregiver understand how your voice, participation, and "stop" and "start" will help you, improve the teamwork, and the outcome.

SECTION 4

TRAIN TO MAINTAIN

CHAPTER 28
Key Points and Application: You Can Do It

Life is not pain-free. As long as you live, you will feel discomfort. Messages travel through your mind that either build you up or break you down. Change requires retraining the body and mind. Your thoughts impact every part of your life. Your brain is pliant with a remarkable ability to heal and grow.

Let's look at what we covered:

1. Remember that reactive living (impulsive emotion-driven words and actions without thinking about the facts or effects on yourself or others) often results in painful surprises. *Reactive* means other people and external circumstances control your thoughts, words, emotions, choices, and actions.

2. Responsive living (measured, proactive, planned problem-prevention, balanced and controlled thinking, and emotions that carefully consider the effects of thoughts, words, and actions on self and others) produces peace, clarity, effectiveness, and positive results. Which type of living do you want? Choose and practice responsive, balanced mindset and discipline.

3. Your reticular activating system (RAS) reinforces the beliefs and values you hold consciously or subconsciously. Look for the good in life and others. Do not grumble or complain about what you do not have. Express gratitude frequently for what you *do* have. Train your brain to

discern the messages from the four voices. Reject lies and useless words. Replace harmful statements with positive truths for more joy, peace, and healthy relationships.

4. Practice O-C-A (Options-Choice-Action) throughout your day with small and large questions. If you feel confused or unsure of your options, ask, and clarify. O-C-A smoothes your decision-making, saves time and energy, and provides better results.

5. Frequent *joy* experiences equip you to become stronger and more resilient through stress. Stress is part of life. Here are some healthful hints to decrease stress:

    a. Don't "what if." Deal with life as it happens. Don't worry and fuss over what might happen. Remember that 85–95% of all the things you worry about never happen. FEAR (False Evidence Appearing Real) causes excessive fight-flight-fear reactions when there is no threat. Don't cause yourself unnecessary anguish by fretting over what you cannot control.

    b. What you believe determines the choices you make and the life you lead. What you believe is what you live.

    c. Don't make a life sentence out of a snapshot event. Most often, a sneeze is just a sneeze. Blow your nose, get the dust out, B-M-W, and get on with life. Too many people experience discomfort and instantly think something is wrong. They rush to a doctor, get diagnosed, and live down to the label they receive. Many aches are normal and temporary. Deal with the moment instead of jumping to the conclusion that requires costly medication and prolonged treatment that may not be needed.

    d. Examine the pain's message. You perceive pain through signals associated with the cause, the cure, and your identity. Some people have obvious, severe tissue damage or age-related deterioration, yet they can function without reporting pain. Other people complain of horrific pain when all tissues appear healthy and no physical cause can be found. Pain with no physical origin or cure points to past trauma and deep non-physical wounds as the possible source. Examine what your pain means to you so all causes of your symptoms can be addressed.

e. Attitude counts. Your attitude, motives, desires, and goals trigger your reticular activating system to look for confirming evidence and support for your expectations. Whether you say you can't, or you can, you are right. Your contentment depends on your mental attitude and outlook.

f. Practice being still and quiet. Spend at least a couple of hours each day with your devices turned off or muted. Read. Take a walk. B-M-W while listening to calming music. Listen to or read God's Word and pray. Lie on your back, watch the clouds, listen to the silence. Don't allow technology and your devices to become your idol and master.

The Source of Joy

Joy will not fall out of the sky and land on your head like a blanket. Deep contentment and joy do not come from the outside but rather from the inside. Joy is a spiritual quality beyond outside influences. The Mayo Clinic reports a tiny percentage of people's statements of joy is due to circumstances.[25] Science tells us pure joy (deep unconditional happiness) does not depend on whimsical conditions. Instead, it depends upon how a person thinks and perceives the world and others. Your joy strength comes from knowing and trusting our Creator Jesus. Here are some suggestions to help you build internal joy and resiliency:

❑ **Get to know and have a personal relationship with your Creator.** Read God's Word, the Bible. You must learn about Him before you can trust Him and His promises. We cannot know true peace and joy outside of close connection with our Creator Jesus. Surround yourself with people who know, honor, and follow Jesus.

❑ **Schedule time with safe family and friends**. Practice being yourself with people who can also be themselves with you. Play board or card games, do outdoor activities together, hike, bike, dance, read and discuss books, have conversations, laugh together, play ball, blow bubbles, play tag, enjoy healthy fun.

❑ **Turn off all devices**. Spend face-to-face time with family or friends. Be fully present at the moment with people. Listen with your head and your heart. Ask questions. Give the gift of letting others know you hear them and connect with them.

❑ **Appreciate what you have**. The sun is shining, you are alive, and the day holds promise if you look for it. Be grateful for vibrant color, breath-taking beauty, delightful tastes, fragrant aromas, and friendly hugs. People don't like to be around a complainer. Practice an attitude of gratitude for small and large blessings. It is nearly impossible to be depressed or feel like a victim when grateful for necessities, abilities, and blessings.

❑ **Maintain an optimistic outlook**. Set your RAS (reticular activating system) to look forward and upward. Reject negative, demeaning, self-limiting, and God-limiting messages. Remember that your thoughts form your words, but your words also have the power to change your thoughts. Choose an active, upward, life-giving cycle instead of a passive downward life-taking spiral.

❑ **Find a purpose in life**. Ask your Creator Jesus to show you the purpose He has planned for you. Our Lord promises in the Bible, "For I know the plans that I have for you,' declares the LORD, 'plans for welfare and not for calamity to give you a future and a hope. Then you will call upon Me and come and pray to Me, and I will listen to you. You will seek Me and find [Me] when you search for Me with all your heart." (Jeremiah 29:12–13). Don't miss out on all your Creator has for you. Volunteer to help others. Share what you know and what you have learned over the years. Step into opportunities and see how God provides for you and grows you.

❑ **Live in the moment**. Remember the phrase, "it came to pass." Troubles come and go. They last as long as they last. The length of trouble is not as significant as how you deal with your difficulties. You may have heard, "The past is history, the future is a mystery, and today is a present—make the most of it." Put your confidence in our Almighty Creator to show you the way and supply all you need.

We have seen how your brain processes your experiences, beliefs, and sensory input to determine your feelings, meanings, choices, and responses. We found that feelings are processed first and fast. However, in non-threatening conditions, emotions are not *leadership qualified*. Now, let's take a closer look at our emotional side.

PART FOUR

YOUR POWERFUL EMOTIONS

*"To get the full value of joy you must
have someone to divide it with."*
Mark Twain

"Don't cry because it's over, smile because it happened."
Dr. Seuss

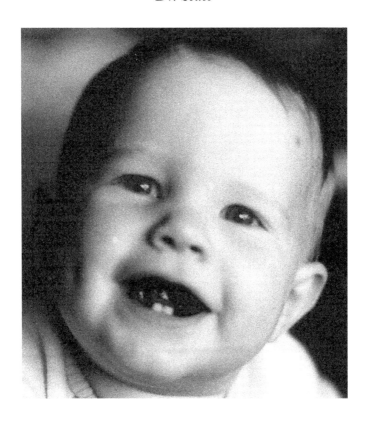

CHAPTER 29
Emotions — Not Leadership Qualified

Why do we associate emotions like love, grief, compassion, and others with our hearts? Could it be because those emotions affect your heart rate, blood pressure, and adrenaline level? Interestingly, in some cultures, the gut is seen as the seat of emotion. Maybe you recognize knots in your stomach when you feel fear, insecurity, embarrassment, or performance stress.

Our emotions guide the verbal and non-verbal messages we accept. Suppose you receive healthy, consistent, harmonious tones, facial expressions, and safe touch in concert with nurturing care. In that case, you interpret the world through feelings of safety, trust, value, confidence, and secure identity. In contrast, when you experience conflicting messages, abuse, neglect, and betrayal, you perceive life through distrust, self-defense, insecurity, and fear.

As we discussed, the brain's threat assessment generates the first and most influential meanings to the thousands of messages received daily. That mental threat assessment is high speed and high impact, whether the threat is real or misinterpreted. If the stimulus gets filtered through pain-colored glasses—perspective distorted by unresolved past wounds—the powerful associated emotion colors the accepted message with prior history instead of current facts.

Whether the accepted message is based on truth or misconceptions, the resulting emotional wave can drown out reason.

Emotions energize our purpose with passion and transfer beliefs from head to heart. How we feel shows in our facial muscles, body language, tone of voice, and the look in our eyes. Emotional expressions from others guide our emotional responses. As gifts from our Creator—emotions connect us to Him and each other. Emotions highlight the purpose and empower action. Feelings enrich our relationships as colors brighten our world, and as flavors enhance our food.

God created human beings for relationship. Relationships help us flourish in a mutual give-and-take with each other, sharing our burdens and joys. Selfless care, encouragement, protection, and support cause us to grow in knowing our Creator in spirit and truth. In our Creator's perfect purpose, we learn to love what He loves, hate what He hates, understand the difference, and stand firm against every kind of evil. If it sounds strange to think that God hates, understand that if you love someone—care so intensely you would give your life to protect them from harm—then you hate anything that hurts or destroys that person. It is an example of emotion giving meaning, depth, and power to a choice.

CHAPTER 30

Defining Emotion: Give Passion to Your Purpose

What is emotion? The scientific community thought emotion centered in the brain's limbic region. But current research indicates that it is not limited to one area of the brain. While the limbic area determines the meaning and priority of sensory messages, emotion seems to impact most brain and mental functions. Therefore, these findings support a new premise.

Kenneth Dodge states, ". . . all information processing is emotional, in that emotion is the energy that drives, organizes, amplifies, and attenuates cognitive activity and in turn, is the experience and expression of this activity."[26] The attempt to separate cognition from emotion is detrimental to our understanding of the mind and mental processes. Instead of considering emotion as bursts of experienced sensations we express, Dr. Daniel Siegel, in his book, *The Developing Mind— How Relationships and the Brain Interact to Shape Who We Are*, asks us to "consider that emotions represent dynamic processes created within the socially influenced, value-appraising processes of the brain."[27]

How our emotions govern us depend on many factors, including personality, motive, maturity, and experience. Feelings connect various systems to form a "state of mind' through which we relate to others. Again, Dr. Siegel says that "'emotions' are proposed to be 'changes' in the state of integration."[28] Better integration results in improved overall well-being.[29] We define integration as the connection between systems or parts of a system.[30] Just as threads of a rope tightly connected are more substantial than a single strand alone, integration means that systems are working together in harmony.

The healthy unity of physical response with what you think, feel, and believe allows you to function as a whole like that rope made up of many strands. With strands aligned in the same direction and working closely together, the rope is strong and withstands mighty forces. In life, the rope indicates a well-integrated function resulting in productivity, resiliency, and effectiveness. Without that unity, the rope is frayed and much weaker. The strands, like independent systems, can only function minimally.

Children raised in healthy, safe, nurturing environments tend to develop robust internal and social responses. These are consistent with building healthy relationships, exercising emotional stability, and exhibiting resiliency during difficulties. The safe nurtured child has a more harmonious system integration or "wholeness." However, a child raised in a threatening, inconsistent, abusive situation experiences less system integration and synchronization. Often, they become entangled in relationships full of conflict, unhealthy boundaries, and mixed messages.

No family is perfect. We have individual levels of integration and maturity. Our maturity and integration levels improve as we examine our overall health and relational dynamics and make healthy corrections. We also heal and grow as we seek and enjoy a community with healthy people. If wounds, error messages, and denial remain unattended, your integration (and thus your life) will remain limited, fractured, and unstable.

Pain-Colored Glasses

Imagine looking through a window or pair of glasses that are covered with dirt and spattered with mud. Your vision would be incomplete, distorted, and inaccurate. You might recognize something wrong with what you see, but you might not identify your error messages. Just as we go for eye exams to obtain prescription glasses to correct visual distortions, we need a healthy perspective to question reactive statements, and to integrate and mature.

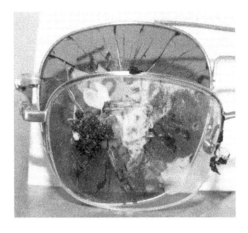

"Pain-colored glasses" describes a life outlook distorted by deep-seated unattended wounds of heart, mind, and spirit. Distorted and limited by the cracks and debris of past pain, vision through pain-colored glasses accepts lies, frustrated hopes, shattered dreams, and misconceptions. Regular events often aggravate deep injuries that cloud experience with faulty messages and strong detrimental emotions.

Too often, people are willing to miss seeing through clean, clear glasses (healing) because they fear revisiting pain and correcting belief errors. Instead, clinging to old familiar pain, they deny their distorted thinking by saying they are "fine." Wearing pain-colored glasses through life keeps bad feelings and injuries suppressed inside and rejects the joy, freedom, and wholeness healing brings. Life becomes a cycle of pain, victimization, and disappointment, which only magnifies wounds and compounds distorted perceptions of threat, helplessness, and isolation.

ॐ ॐ ॐ ॐ ॐ

Here's an exercise to experience these concepts. Print three different patterns on transparent film. Each pattern represents an effect of trauma:

1. Wounds—this transparency has a printed pattern, which clutters the transparency
2. Lies—this transparency has a different printed pattern, which alters the visual field
3. Denial—this transparency is solid black, which darkens and makes the film opaque.

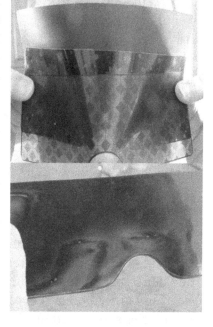

As you look through each transparency, observe how the pattern clutter distorts your vision. Notice how you perceive normal life and reality around you. When you add three layers together and attempt to see through them, you can't. You don't have a frame of reference for your surroundings: Are you safe? Alone? Unsure of how you feel or should respond? This exercise illustrates why past wounds and trauma increase physical, mental, and emotional defense and stress.

Now, position yourself near a light source and put all three transparency layers together. Look through the layers with the printed (dull) side away from you. Now, with the shiny side toward you, hold these representations of lies, wounds, and denial (the transparency layers) in front of your face. What do you see? Yourself. Without addressing deep, internal wounds and lies, you focus on yourself. Self-centered thinking leads you to be a victim and blame others for your responsibilities or take the blame for others' choices. Self-focus makes you more sensitive to offense and rejection from others when unintended, and you feed personal pain and lies.

In a presentation made by Colin Ross, MD, he asserted that "trauma is an obstacle in normal human development," which results in less system integration, unity, and maturity. When we see clearly, we have an accurate base to evaluate and make the best decisions. However, if we view ourselves, others, God, experiences, and life through the distortions of pain-colored glasses, our harbored hurts, bitterness, resentment, anger, despair, hopelessness, lies, and denial continue to cause us and others more pain.

How much joy do you feel daily? Do you simply exist? Or do you feel passion and purpose? Do you wish things could be better? Understand there are hope and healing available. Check out the resources section at the back of this book or contact me. Don't give up! Look for a counselor, physician, pastor, or mentor whose life exhibits the values, wisdom, joy, freedom, and healthy relationships you desire. Whether you are hurting, healthy, or a caregiver seeking to help others, treating the entire person is critically essential.

Stress with a Purpose

Life is full of challenges. Circumstances try us, test us, reveal us, and strengthen or weaken us. We receive wounds from others and ourselves. As we review how our brain works, it becomes clear that powerful initial emotions can adhere to or "tag" an overwhelming traumatic experience with a message about self, other people, or God. These emotion-charged messages override reason, especially when the trauma occurred at an early (less integrated) age. Unless the deep wounds heal and the emotional tags are clarified, survivors often view themselves, their Creator, other people, and life events through pain-colored glasses established during traumatic events. These deep wounds fester over time and express themselves in physical, emotional, and relational pain.

Hope Pulls You Through

Hope is critical for survival and endurance through pain and struggles. Hope is not passive wishing and waiting for whatever happens. Hope is active "holding on" and envisioning a better future. Hope is the fuel that pulls broken hearts through to healing. To endure present stresses, you must have hope for a better future. Without hope—the promise, or at least the possibility, of relief, improvement, joy in the future—we easily give up and lose the will to live. Imagining a better future, coupled with a strong desire for that vision, energizes people to persevere through dire circumstances and motivates us to take steps to make those desires real[31].

SECTION 1

DO YOU KNOW?

CHAPTER 31
Your Attitude is Showing

Next time you look in the mirror, stop for a moment. Observe your facial expression. Look at your posture. What nonverbal messages do you see? How do *you* make you feel? This exercise is essential because those around you often reflect the messages you send.

Emotional messages from depression, fear, frustration, insecurity, discontentment, or contentment, confidence, joy, and peace are seen in our physical bodies. The tone of our words powerfully imprints a meaning. Be aware of your body language and the attitude you express nonverbally. Avoid personal hurt and offense by calming your emotions, mind, and body (Remember B-M-W: Breathe-Melt-Wiggle) as you clarify any hurtful or inconsistent messages.

Often, people who have known me for years ask why I don't seem to worry, react in fear, or struggle with depression. They know I have sustained serious physical injuries, come through financial threats and losses, grieved the loss of loved ones and pets, and faced life challenges like anyone else.

> Healthy, mature interaction occurs when your nonverbal expression matches your verbal tone and communication.

Is it just my personality or that I don't feel? No, like you, I experience the full scope of emotions. But I have learned two important facts: 1) Jesus has the map of my life; He is the Source of all I need, and 2) worry, drama, and trying to do life in my strength is exhausting and painful. Rather than help us, drama and adrenaline reactions deplete us and hinder circumstances. Practicing what I preach, I rely on strength, wisdom, and care through my relationship with my Creator, Jesus. Throughout my life, He has always been trustworthy. I know His faithfulness and sufficiency beyond what I can see or understand. While I do what I can to improve the situation, when I have no more control or influence, I make the best of it and trust the outcome to Jesus. I hope you understand this, but if you don't know what I'm talking about, please contact me or find a God-honoring Christian to help you know your Savior, Healer, Protector, Creator, Jesus.

Self-confidence depends on your strength, ability, and endurance. I am not the Savior—I need a Savior. Frequently, things have not happened as I thought or hoped, when I wanted, or in a way I could see. But every time, my Savior brought me through the challenge—often, more smoothly or with a better outcome than I could have imagined. To persevere through future trials, I remember how God brought me through those many seemingly hopeless times beyond my strength and understanding.

Relying on your Creator infuses you with hope, peace, strength, wisdom, and *all* you need. If you can take decisive action, do so in His power, will, way, and time. If you cannot improve the situation, fretting and worrying makes you miserable and wears you out.

SECTION 2
FOOD FOR THOUGHT

CHAPTER 32

Joy is a Goal and a Necessity: You Were Created for JOY

Joy is necessary for optimal human development.[32] Babies sense value, love, and connection through touch, physical care, and facial expression. Nonverbal messages of acceptance in a smiling face, safe touch, and healthy nurture result in joy—the main motivation for children under eighteen months old. We are relational beings. From birth to death, connection with others or lack of that necessary interaction impacts every aspect of our health, thinking, function, and perspective. We need joy. Joy is a necessity for human development.[33] Powerful sources of joy for children and for adults include respect, safety, caring touch, and consistent verbal and non-verbal messages.[34]

Joy experiences reinforce a sense of safety, confidence, potential, and resiliency in times of hardship. Relationship joy improves your health and function as you age.[35] Different from happiness, joy results in positive growth and health beyond the circumstances. Joy promotes healthy choices and lifestyle, boosts your immune system, decreases pain and stress, and supports longevity.[36]

Receiving messages (such as "I am glad to see you," "I am pleased to be with you," and "You are valued") creates joy. Maybe you experienced ethereal joy when you felt cherished, deeply peaceful, and contented. These memories could be of your first love, smothering kisses from a child or puppy, the birth of a child, or enjoying a relaxing, beautiful place with a loved one. These almost indescribable feelings of ecstasy register in the right hemisphere of your brain and result in the growth of your joy center—the Right Orbital Prefrontal Cortex (ROPC).

Let's review

When receiving sensory information through sight, sound, touch, smell, or taste, the amygdala filters the stimulus to initially determine the threat level. The less ability a person has to protect themselves or understand the stimuli, the higher the threat perceived. Whether accurate or not, the defense messages and meanings are ingrained and persist over time. Children are especially vulnerable to dissociation and retaining distorted perspectives beyond the trauma into adulthood because they lack the power to protect themselves. They have less truth and joy-based experiences to help them deal with danger and trauma.

This diagram summarizes the cycle of distorted information (through pain-colored glasses) from past trauma affecting current situations when there is no threat:

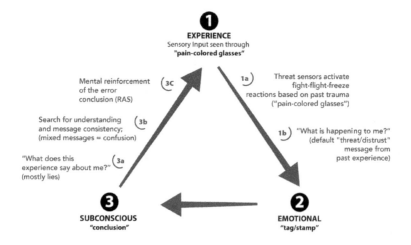

1a) With a history of unresolved trauma, normal, sight, sound, smell, touch, and taste information flood the hypersensitive threat assessment area of the brain, which consciously or unconsciously reminds the survivor of past real or perceived danger. Retained messages and meaning from these past experiences result in fight-flight-freeze reactions. The past feelings and emotions overpower rational problem-solving and reality judgment.

1b) The pain-colored glasses mix the present experience with past wounds and interpretations, which distort the meaning of what is currently happening.

2) This overlay of past emotional tags (from previous neglect, abuse, trauma, or hurtful misunderstanding) onto a present safe situation increases confusion, distrust, and feelings of being unsafe. For instance, being in a typical, non-threatening crowd of people in a mall or at a conference might be perceived through pain-colored glasses as dangerous, trapped, suffocated, or attacked. A caring hug intended to comfort and connect may be misinterpreted and felt in the same harmful way.

3) When a person has a history of mixed messages and inconsistent unsafe relationships, healthy, safe interaction cannot be recognized or received and, at worst, the exact opposite of the intended-action results. The safe, caring event is twisted into condemning, threatening, controlling, or rejecting.

3a) Distorted conclusions impact a person's identity perpetuating lies, accusations, entitlement, blame, victimization, and lack of value.

3b) Identity confusion regarding self and God steals peace and joy, hinders confidence, and magnifies lies and negative perceptions.

3c) The reticular activating system (RAS) highlights confirming incoming information for established perceptions. Without healing, self-persecution, lies, pain, and victimization reinforce seeing life through pain-colored glasses.

Intentionally or not, distorted messages sent and received cause hurt people to hurt people. Unattended harbored hurts are minefields that can initiate unhealthy reactions in social settings and relationships. Just as with visual acuity problems, deep internal wounds, whether recognized or not, worsen without healing. They also improve with healing, treatment, and training to correct perspectives, choices, and habits.

Now, let's look at the same cycle of information-processing without pain-colored glasses:

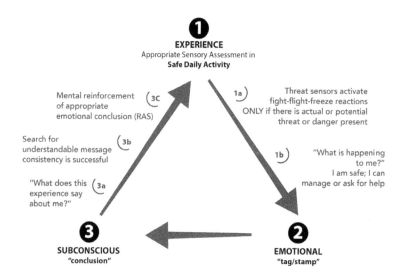

We find:

1) The same common, daily, non-threatening sensory stimulus enters the brain.

1a) The information gets checked for an actual or potential threat. Recognized as non-threatening and manageable, and it doesn't initiate the fight-flight-freeze reaction.

1b) The question "What is happening to me?" gets quickly and peacefully answered in the unified, integrated brain and body. "Nothing unusual. I know who I am. I am safe, familiar with my surroundings, and this activity. I know how to respond appropriately."

2) Maybe there is an emotional tag like, "I love that song— it reminds me of a joyful time," or "I remember feeling that fear before, but I was able to get through it with the help of

God." Maybe there is no emotion attached to the situation and activity, but there is peace. No drama, no stress.

3) Understandable messages emerge as the thousands of sensory messages are received, sorted, and connected based on cohesive sensory experience combined with cognitive information. This harmony of experience with cognitive understanding and current circumstances results in a subconscious conclusion that reinforces an accurate perspective. When mental knowledge, emotional consistency, and physical experience are appropriate and harmonious, reacting turns into reasoning. Confusion is questioned, reality is assessed correctly, problems are solved, fears are resolved, and emotions are channeled to help instead of hinder. This balance of cognitive information with emotional patience prevents overreaction. A suitable response results from a measured, reasonable assessment of the situation combined with consistent, understandable information.

SECTION 3

LET'S DO THIS!

CHAPTER 33

Train Your Emotions: Are You Paralyzed or Empowered?

Our emotions are the arrows that reveal and point to our belief system. How we feel gives dimension to our life experiences. Therefore, emotions can paralyze or empower us.

As multiple colors magnify our sense of beauty and the variety of tastes enhance our food enjoyment, the emotional spectrum allows us to deeply experience the joy of a sunrise with a mountaintop panorama, belly-laugh during play with loved ones, or express compassion for each other when we share deep grief or painful trials. Emotions add embellishment and dimension, but they cannot take the place of facts and reality. Pain-colored glasses warp beauty, darken hope, and focus on held hurts instead of available joy, connection, help, and healing. These glasses (created from past trauma, embedded lies, and misconceptions) distort current events, messages, interactions, and others' intentions.

> Emotions are mostly non-conscious processes that prepare us for action (motion).[37]

✂︎ ✂︎ ✂︎ ✂︎ ✂︎

I was privileged to support a group of women who had survived extreme childhood trauma and sexual abuse. As we became acquainted, the women eventually shared they did not know how my support could benefit them because I had not experienced the horrors they lived through. Thanking them for their honesty, openness, and courage, I asked the group questions about how they saw the future. Overall, these women felt they were stuck—their painful past clung to them like a muddy wet shirt. The future held no hope for change. These women believed they could only survive with the shadow of past hurt, lies, and shame hovering over them.

Although I had not experienced what they had, I let the group know I felt angry and heartbroken because of their suffering. I asked if they believed life could improve. Did they think a coach or guide could help them receive and achieve healing? After further conversation, these survivors discovered healing and restoration was possible through healthy experience with guidance and support.

A healthy person with a heart to help can serve as a guide. This person demonstrates healthy boundaries, provides safe nurture and support, shares options not previously seen or considered, and teaches balanced responses that replace past reactions caused by pain-colored glasses. A healthy guide offers safety while exploring and unifying facts with emotional reactions. Deep, past, internal injuries heal as the hurt person is guided, equipped, and empowered to move forward in the hope and healing available.

প্রু প্রু প্রু প্রু প্রু

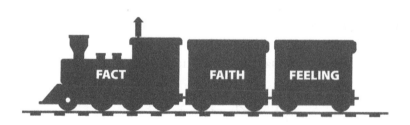

Imagine that you function as a train where fact provides realistic options for your choice of direction toward your desired goal. Your fact engine powers you up challenging hills and through obstacles, brakes for control down the mountain, and keeps you on the tracks. Your fact engine has large wheels to solidly connect to the tracks of objective reality, safety, and traction. The fact engine lights realistic options and direction, keeps your life on track toward the goal, and leads the boxcar of faith and the caboose of feeling.

If the feeling caboose leads the train, the whole train races backward, and derails quickly without fact's provision of light, weight, and power, which keep the entire train (you) on track to the goal. Feeling enhances and cements our perspectives but has no compass or basis in reality without fact. The fact engine directs feeling in a positive direction. Don't let feelings lead your actions or control your thinking.

The boxcar of faith in your Creator is the basis of truth. Faith builds trust in His wisdom and power which is far greater than yours. Faith—trust in His unconditional love, all-knowing wisdom, and total sufficiency—powerfully, positively impacts your life train. We'll unpack this concept in-depth in *Part 5— The Missing Peace.*

The 5 A's of Healthy Response

The more intense and instantaneous the emotion you feel in a non-life-threatening situation, the more critical it is to STOP. Take a few moments to let your brain balance strong feelings with facts, consequences, options, and reason. Sometimes feelings startle or scare you. That is an excellent time to STOP to B-M-W.

Here are five steps to balance your emotions with truth and reality. When you feel strong emotion or want to change a habitual reaction:

1. **Acknowledge.** Consider what you feel in your body, mind, spirit, emotions, and whether you are in control

or controlled by circumstances, other people, or outside influences. Take a moment to B-M-W. Calm and connect yourself while recognizing how information or situations affect you.

2. **Ask.** "Which of the four voices do I hear now (or most)?" 1) The voice of my flesh defends or justifies my feelings and desires, regardless of reality or what may be best for me and others. 2) The accuser Satan (enemy of God and His people) feeds me lies which attack my God-given identity and God's character. Satan lies to me to build doubt, fear, and isolation so that I feel alone without hope or help from God or anyone else. 3) The voice of the world tells me what I should or should not do to please people who may not even know me or care about me. Too often, I mistake the world's voice for the voice of a friend. But its values and systems use me for its interests and seek to control me. A true friend wants what is best for me and protects me. 4) The voice of my Creator reminds me that I am not alone—He is with me always—He cares for me and the details of my life. He can get me through every pain and problem in my life. Is the message I hear the truth or a lie? I need and want my Creator's voice to be the one I hear and follow consistently.

3. **Avoid.** Don't rationalize (rational-lies), overanalyze, justify, or feed your emotional reactions. B-M-W as you carefully face and evaluate circumstances and how you are affected. Let facts and objective scrutiny guide your responses and choices.

4. **Attend.** Listen to your body. What does it need? Take inventory. Care for yourself as you would care for a precious child or a loved one in discomfort. What would soothe your gut, back, neck, head, and heart? Take a moment to care for yourself or improve the situation.

5. **Attitude.** Your attitude and beliefs dictate your outlook. A negative attitude focuses your reticular activating system (RAS) on searching for supporting harmful

data that ruins your day. Conversely, if you focus on appreciating what is good, your outlook, health, and day improve.[38, 39] Ask for help when you struggle to make positive changes.

Going through the 5 A's of Healthy Response, you train your mind, body, spirit, and emotions to respond appropriately by connecting reality to your situation. You can then evaluate conditions, see options, decide wisely, and maintain healthy control.

Refusing Joy

Since beliefs shape the way you live, examine the foundation and source of those beliefs to determine if they agree with reality, follow our Creator's instructions, and are beneficial or detrimental.

- Do you accept self-limiting messages?
- Do you believe flattering, desirable, yet dangerous lies?
- How well does your mental "delete button" work?
- Can you gratefully accept an uncomfortable, corrective, helpful truth?

Recognize valuable messages and reject junk messages. There is no hope of correction or improvement unless you honestly and objectively examine the source and the accuracy of the messages coming into your mind.

Consistently feeling distressed, neglected, or unsafe depletes your joy center and causes the delete button in your brain to become reversed. Deep hurt and an unrelenting sense of threat make you defensive. Your adrenaline and stress levels stay elevated, causing an overworked fight-flight-freeze reaction. In this no-threat, unhealthy condition, your defenses are up, you are unnecessarily wary, distrusting, and on guard. The result? Your mental junk filter and delete button become reversed—you store negative thoughts and beliefs and reject helpful positive input.

Joy, peace, rest, and trust are foreign to you unless you have experienced those blessings. For hearts, minds, spirits, and bodies repeatedly wounded, those qualities our Creator intended to be natural elements of daily life are strange, unfamiliar, and frightening. While unhealthy existence remains undesirable, it is *familiar*. The wounded RAS filter expects mistreatment, danger, and betrayal. The traumatized brain rejects hope, healing, and caring support. Instead, this wounded brain accepts and retains all the painful and discouraging messages that reinforce history. The RAS filter focuses on and collects negative input. The mental delete button keeps harmful messages and rejects the hopeful healing ones. When the survivor takes the first step toward healing, this cycle begins to correct.

Do you know people who appear miserable, smile little, and always seem burdened by life? They lack joy, energy, passion, and purpose. Maybe that's how you see your life. Fear, anxiety, worry, and discontent seem to rule our society. You may forget or not even realize that  you have options in how you choose to think. Our perceptions and emotions can change. Victim mentality says, "I don't have a choice," "nothing will change," or "this is all there is" without wondering if these thoughts and statements are even true.

Consider whether you are receiving or refusing the joy available to you. When you haven't experienced much joy, it isn't easy to receive care or pleasure. Remember that hurt people hurt people. When you have not healed from deep hurts, you tend to hold onto the familiar bad stuff (lies, wounds, distrust, defensive tension) and push away the *available* good stuff (joy, trust, truth, peace, rest, support, care) that others wish to share.

When you attend to healing your internal wounds and replace lies with truth, you desire more healing, and your joy builds. Safety, connection, support, and healthy friendship replace isolation and defensiveness. Your emotional reactions become appropriate self-controlled responses based on rational assessment and problem-solving. You can transform a stressed life into the peace, joy, choice, and efficient function of a blessed life.

How would more joy, connection, health, and peace change your life? The answer is priceless.

SECTION 4

TRAIN TO MAINTAIN

CHAPTER 34

Live It! JOY: Do You Want More Joy?

Though it is hard to change long-standing habits, it's well worth your effort to maximize the amount of real joy you receive and share with others. We know joy positively impacts your health—body, mind, and soul. In safety, practice the following principles and keep a record of new joys you see and receive. On a calendar or in a journal, write down the effects of those experiences.

If you missed out on childhood joys, take time to enjoy things you missed:

- Go fishing
- Blow bubbles
- Play ball
- Color
- Do crafts or athletics
- Play a musical instrument
- Enjoy board games with others
- Play in the snow
- Make s'mores at the campfire

Look for healthy joy and participate!

When you communicate with others, your tone, facial expression, and body language send more powerful messages than your words. Take a moment to B-M-W, ask your Creator to help you respond to people in His will, way, and Word.[40]

Ask your family and friends to help you monitor your tone. When communication feels uncomfortable in our family, we say, "Would you please say that another way?" Let your words and body language be life-giving, not life-taking.

Let's review.

The stronger the emotions you feel, the more critical it is to check those emotions' accuracy with current facts and intentions. Use B-M-W to calm yourself and assess the situation objectively. Respond with self-control. Don't let others and external factors control your reactions. Build healthy habits with the 5 A's of Healthy Response:

- *Acknowledge* what you feel in your body, mind, spirit, and emotions.
- *Ask* which voice you hear? The voice of your flesh, enemy, world, or Creator? Is the message truth or a lie?
- *Avoid* rationalizing (rational lies) or over-analyzing. If facts don't support your emotion, re-train your emotions to be appropriate and consistent with reality. Let data and objective scrutiny guide your choices and responses.
- *Attend* to your needs. Listen to your body. What would comfort your gut, muscles, head, and heart? Call someone and receive the care and relief that your body, mind, and spirit desire. You are not alone. Ask our Lord and Savior for wisdom and to satisfy your needs.

> The very nature of joy makes nonsense of our common distinction between having and wanting. —C.S. LEWIS

- *Attitude* is critical for your overall health and ability to receive joy. Listen to uplifting music, count your blessings, look for the beauty around you. Keep uplifting Scripture and list of recent victories handy to reflect on and remember. Ask for help when it is challenging to change your attitude and make healthy choices.

For more information on these subjects:

 Check out Videos, blogs, and other resources at 4x4Healing.com.

Live It! Trauma Distorts Reality: Pain-Colored Glasses

Picture yourself at your favorite place on a glorious sunny day. The air is crisp and clear. Sky and flowers are brilliant colors. With all your senses—with your eyes, ears, nose, skin, and tongue—you savor the messages sent to your brain.

Suddenly, a thick fog rolls in and surrounds you. You are safe and calm, but you can hardly see your hand in front of your face. It's dusk, and, as the light of day fades, your vision becomes cloudier and darker. Your friends and loved ones find you in your fog. They run up to you, arms wide to give you big hugs. But all you see are shadowy, fuzzy human shapes approaching fast. How do you feel? How do you react? When your eyesight is clouded, and you cannot quickly understand what is happening, fear, old perceptions, feelings, and defenses take over. Joy is lost.

Once you can see clearly, you assess the situation accurately. You determine you are safe with nothing to fear. You recognize what is happening and decide how to respond. You can run up to the people running toward you and share warm hugs. Or, if you want more control in this energetic event, you shout, "Hey, slow down! Don't run me over!" With a clear understanding of intention and reality, you freely receive and share multiplied joy!

Change Unhealthy Habits

If you desire to change unhealthy habits, patterns, reactions, and situations in your life, an excellent place to start is to write down what is and is not working in your life. In self-exploration, journaling helps you to identify and reflect on the facts, feelings, and perspectives that contribute to the familiar patterns of reactions, responses, and choices you are living.

To change a habit, you must start with your thinking. How does that happen? Replacement is the key, but there is a necessary order. When the desired lifestyle change fails, it is probably due to one or more of the following problems:

- The change is not worth the effort. The change must be more important or valuable than your current mindset, pattern, habit, or choice. Highlight and focus on the benefits to energize you through the work of change. The positive change—the replacement—must be clear and more valuable than the current harmful habit or choice. The higher the substitution value, and the more you desire the change, the greater your chance of success in conquering and replacing the negative thought or behavior.
- The change does not seem possible, productive, or substantially rewarding. List real or imagined hindrances to your positive change. Are there enough frequent rewards and incentives to continue?
- The change is too vague, easily ignored, or habitually inconsistent. Lack of clear goals, accountability, and confusion justify failure.
- The change is not small enough, easily recognized, or simple enough. Small, easily accomplished steps make change more pleasant and possible. Use reminders like the color red or a red dot to remind you to change your thinking and behavior.
- The change is not practiced frequently. Small steps of improvement require frequent and consistent repetition.

CHAPTER 35

Live It! The Benefits of Journaling: Record and Remember

Have you been frustrated when you seek help, but find that those same thoughts, issues, and concerns persist like a cloud of gnats flying around your head? You identify each problem (gnat) and talk with someone about each concern. You feel heard, affirmed, and supported, but the annoyance remains. The issues and concerns (gnats) continue to swarm around and haunt you.

Identify those annoying gnats by swatting them on to paper. Write when each issue started, how the problem impacts your life, along with the meanings and feelings you associate with each situation. Write down—journal—your troubles and share with a trusted professional, friend, or coach to clarify and see options for resolution.

Regularly writing down thoughts, concerns, and feelings about your battles and victories in a daily journal, diary, notebook, or computer document provides a significant opportunity to think through what is happening in your life. What do you feel and understand about your concern? How do people and circumstances affect you? Question, emote, and brainstorm on paper. Short or long, let it all out.

Ten Healthy Results

1. Writing lightens your mental burden. Instead of holding or recycling information in your head, or possibly forgetting, let the journal carry the load.

2. Journaling benefits emotional health. Regular writing helps you become more mindful, more aware of your body, mind, spirit, and emotions. Writing reveals deep inner needs and desires. Journaling brings order, focus, and clarity to facts, feelings, motives, and perspectives.

3. Journaling helps you stay present and maintain a healthy outlook. Journaling provides a mechanism for releasing thoughts, pain, frustrations, anger, fears, hopes, dreams, and desires. It presents an opportunity for emotional catharsis and helps the brain regulate emotions.[41]

4. Studies show that even one hour of writing about distressing events helped participants make sense of the facts and reduce stress.[42]

5. Expressive writing (journaling) for 15 to 20 minutes a day three to five times over four months can lower blood pressure, strengthen the immune system, and improve liver function.[43]

6. Writing reveals hidden things. As you write, problems and options are clarified and understood. Underlying thoughts and insights come to mind. Journaling exposes details that may indicate underlying lies, wounds, fears, mixed messages, or denial. Reflecting on your journaling reveals patterns of choice, habit, and lifestyle.

7. Journaling encourages you to clarify goals, sort and prioritize puzzling pieces, identify hindrances, and track progress.

8. Journaling reminds you of past victories, which provide strength and hope for current and future challenges.

9. Journaling provides personal accountability and energizes forward motion.

10. One writing insight leads to another, connecting emotions, facts, questions, options, and answers.

For more information on these subjects:

 Check out the videos, blogs, and other information at 4x4Healing.com.

Start Your Journal

The hardest part of any healthy discipline is starting. As you begin your journal, you will probably be surprised, amazed, and impressed by the advantages.

1. **Choose your desired type of journal.** Decide on digital or paper. Select a format, frequency, and style you'll enjoy.
2. **Find a quiet place.** Surround yourself with proper support for sitting, creature comforts (fan, blanket, heater), water, good light, facial tissues, or whatever else you need or enjoy. Plan to spend a certain amount of time writing regularly.
3. **Start.** Write down what's on your mind and heart—include your concerns and feelings. How are you affected by these issues? How can you begin to make healthy changes?
4. **Keep it private.** Your heart shares its depth when you feel safe. Keep your writing confidential.
5. **Let it flow.** There is no right or wrong in your writing. Focus on freely releasing what's inside.
6. **Ask God to show you.** Ask Him to reveal His will for your circumstance, concern, and desire. Search Scripture to discover the way He works in similar situations. Remember how He brought you through past trials.
7. **Record victories.** Journal details about how you overcame in past battles. Understand, record, and celebrate each success. Reflecting on your journal and remembering your strengths and God's provision will help you through future trials.

Progression of Healing

Gaining balance in your body, mind, heart, and spirit requires a desire to correct problems. Plus, you learn new ways of thinking, choosing, and living. Learn healthy replacements to heal past wounds and develop functional, healthy, life-giving patterns. Your healing journey means participating in five activities:

1. Recognize that you need and desire both healing and freedom to live victoriously.
2. Choose not to settle for repeated hurt and hopeless cycles. Commit to get help and finish the work of healing. Intentionally look forward during the healing process.
3. Receive support and guidance from competent, caring people, and accept a new way of thinking, making choices, and acting.
4. Practice and exercise new healthy options in thought, word, and deed.
5. Share with others the healing, freedom, joy, victories, and blessings you experience in life and relationships.

Key Points and Summary

- Trauma hinders healthy development. Pain-colored glasses distort current events, interactions, and positive outcomes.
- Powerful emotional triggers and tags associated with past abuse and trauma often overpower rational thought and responses.
- People with unattended deep emotional, mental, and spiritual wounds internalize painful thoughts and feelings, which cause you to block and refuse opportunities for joy, peace, and healthy connection.
- Human beings need and desire to receive and share joy. You were created for joy.
- Journaling is a beneficial, healthy habit.

Do you experience peace and joy daily? If you desire deep, abiding peace and joy, read on.

PART FIVE

THE MISSING PEACE

It is not how much we have, but how much we enjoy,
that makes happiness.
Charles Spurgeon

God cannot give us a happiness and peace apart from
Himself because it is not there. There is no such thing.
C.S. Lewis

CHAPTER 36

Your Core Identity: You Are an Eternal Being

Your spirit is the core of who you are—the essence of your identity. Your spirit lives even after your earthly body turns to dust.

If you have questions about this chapter, please consider a Bible-teaching church, pastor, or Christian friend for help. You can also check out the Resources section at the end of this book.

People say they are Christians, but only those who recognize their need for a Savior, then accept and follow the Lord Jesus Christ as their Savior and Lord are true "Christians."

Following Jesus touches every aspect of life—words, attitudes, decisions, and actions—heart, mind, body, and spirit. A Christian doesn't follow a man-made religious system but enjoys a personal relationship with the triune God—Father, Son, and Holy Spirit—through prayer and following our operating manual—His Word, the Bible. A Christian not only believes in Jesus Christ, the only Son of God, Messiah, Savior, Lord, but also honors and obeys Him. Just like a grapevine branch cannot live or produce fruit apart from the vine and root, a Christian cannot and chooses not to function apart from God's Word, will, way, and time. The Holy Spirit of God lives in each of Jesus' followers, directing and providing everything needed for our intended purpose and ultimate fulfillment.

Maybe you believe there is nothing after death. But if there is existence after death and you die in your sin (disregard of and disobedience to God) without repentance (heart-felt remorse and turning from that sin), and without accepting Jesus' payment of His death on the cross for our sin, you lose everything on earth and in eternity. Jesus makes it clear in Scripture there are only two destinations after death:

1. Eternal misery and separation from God in a fiery place called hell OR
2. In God's presence with joy, peace, and paradise forever in a place called heaven.

Each person's decision to receive or reject the Lord Jesus Christ determines where he or she will spend eternity. Sin leads to its penalty—death.[44] Will you choose to exist in your strength and limited understanding, wrestling pain and trials, refusing the only One who can save you? Or will you realize there is nothing you can do to earn your way to heaven? Will you surrender your will to the Lord Jesus, accept His payment of death on the cross to pay for your sin, and be forgiven?[45] Remember—*no decision is a decision.*

How does that work? Your Creator loves you. He wants a close relationship (not religion) with each human being. But true love must have a choice because love does not result from pressure, coercion, or manipulation. Love, loyalty, worship, and trust must come as a choice from deep inside you. God has chosen to love you—no matter what. How will you respond?

If you decide you don't need God or want a Savior, God will honor your choice. You're on your own. Your destiny is hell—but you can change your future by accepting the gift of forgiveness and eternal life that Jesus offers. When you humble yourself and accept Jesus' gift of life and sacrifice, you desire to honor Him and live by His Word.

Even as you do God's will and fulfill your God-given purpose, trials and difficulties will occur. Plug into the *Source of your identity, value, purpose, and joy* for strength, endurance, hope, and resiliency beyond human understanding and capability.

Feeling discouraged, rejected, or powerless is normal when your dreams and efforts get hindered. Instead of succumbing to despair, giving up, or settling back into your unfulfilling comfort zone, consider that your hardships may be affirmations that your work is important. Press on in the strength of our Savior to the finish with determination! (In your Bible, read James 1:2-4).

Trials reveal your need for a Savior. Adversity presents you with a choice: Will you choose to try managing alone on the my-way-highway OR turn to your Savior to depend on His endless wisdom, power, resources, and direction? Your trust in Jesus through life's challenges proves your faith in Jesus' promise to get you through.

> There is nothing you can do on this earth that the Creator, Lord Jesus cannot forgive if you genuinely repent. The only way God cannot forgive you is if *you will not accept* His forgiveness.

> The harder it is to do what pleases Jesus, the more important it is to get that job done. Your victory (joy, healing, blessing, calling, and freedom) is at stake.

Will you be a perfect Christian?

No! Christians are not perfect; they are forgiven. Christians desire to please God at all times, but when they make mistakes and recognize their disobedience in thoughts, words, and actions—which grieve God's heart—Christians repent (feel genuine sorrow which turns them away from disobedience and back to God). In repentance, forgiveness, and dependence on God, you experience the freedom, peace, and joy of living under the umbrella of Jesus' direction, provision, and protection.

Some people think Jesus was a good man who was an excellent example for us to follow to get into heaven. If you believe that, you must live the same sinless life which completely honors and obeys Father God. Have you ever lied or stolen anything? Have your thoughts and motives ever been selfish or impure? If you scrutinize your life, you find you have disobeyed God in thought, word, and deed. That is sin.

If what you believe is not true, do you want to know the truth?

Since the payment for sin is death, we cannot pay for our sins—every person needs a Savior. Imagine if you were to get into heaven, you must jump from New York to Paris. No matter how hard you try, you cannot make it. You must accept a ticket on Savior Airlines—Jesus is the pilot who is able to get you there. Just as if you were drowning in the ocean, you would need someone to lift you out of the water and put you on dry ground. You cannot save yourself.

My deepest desire is that you experience a genuine, safe, gratifying relationship with the One who created you. What keeps you from accepting the Messiah Jesus as your Savior and Lord?

Heaven and hell are real. Heaven is a place of peace, love, joy, kindness, patience, purpose, goodness, contentment, and closeness to God. Hell is a place of burning pain, torment, and eternal separation from God—a place of utter misery. It is your choice to accept Jesus' gift of life, payment for your sin, forgiveness, and eternity in heaven or reject Him for the my-way-highway to hell.[46]

What separates people from their Creator? Willful disobedience and rejection of God and His instruction, which is for our good. "Sin" means "disregard for God."

Maybe pride, fear, or lies keep you from seeking or accepting God's mercy and precious gift of eternal life. God wants all people to come to Him. He knows we need help, and He provided the way.[47] Our Savior laid down His life and took it up again three days later. More than 500 people saw Him alive[48] after His gruesome torture and death.[49] Jesus intentionally gave His life in our place—an act of love even though people rejected Him—so all of humankind might come back to Him.[50]

No matter what we've done or endured, our Creator wants to forgive, cleanse, and restore us. But each of us must receive it actively, by:

1. Wanting to be cleansed, healed, and renewed

2. Turning from self-centered, rebellious ways
3. Asking the Lord Jesus Christ for cleansing and forgiveness
4. Surrendering your my-way-highway to Jesus' absolute control in the small and huge things in life
5. Searching His Word, seeking His strength, growing with His people in His will, way, and Word.[51]

Your Creator honors your choice to reject Him or follow Him. Our life on this earth is for each person to choose their eternal destiny.

> *"So, fear the LORD and serve him wholeheart-*
> *edly. Put away forever the idols your ancestors*
> *worshiped when they lived beyond the Euphrates*
> *River and in Egypt. Serve the LORD alone.*
> *But if you refuse to serve the LORD, then*
> *choose today whom you will serve. ...*
> *But as for me and my family, we will serve*
> *the LORD." Joshua 24:14-15 NLT*

It is vital that we rightly understand the principles in God's Word. We can know the proper meaning through careful examination of the original author's intent, language, and cultural perspective. Then, we must correctly apply Biblical principles to our thoughts, words, and deeds.

Questions to consider:

- Do I want to see and be all my Creator intended for me?
- Am I willing to accept my Creator's gifts of forgiveness and restoration?
- How will my thought, words, and actions show that Jesus is the LORD of my life?
- How will I commit to read and follow God's Word (the Bible), His manual for successful living, and our protection?

Here's a handy acronym to help you remember to apply God's Word daily. BIBLE: Basic Instructions Before Leaving Earth

Throughout our lives, we have all ignored our Maker's instruction manual. We've made damaging choices and hurt other people in the process. We need help, forgiveness, and training.[52]

CHAPTER 37

How Jesus Changed My Life: What He Did for Me He Will Do for You

I don't remember a time when I didn't believe in our Creator. However, until my thirties, I traveled the my-way-highway. I knew God was there, but I had things to do and places to go on my strength and agenda.

At thirteen-years-old, while attending a church camp, my spirit became convicted and broken. I realized I couldn't drive my life successfully. I needed and wanted Jesus to be my driver. Through my twenties, I continued to love the Lord but remained spiritually immature. I turned to God last, not first—not understanding what it meant for Jesus to be LORD of my life.

In the 1980s, I bought into the world's lie "I am woman—I can do it all," thinking that as my husband traveled and worked, I could be a great wife, mother, homemaker, and still work 40-60 hours per week at my two-office clinic.

God got my attention in my thirties when I ended up in the hospital, bleeding internally from an antibiotic reaction. My husband and parents were traveling. No family was available to help me with my small children, ages 1 and 6. Close and dear friends took me to the hospital and cared for our children for 2-3 weeks—twice because I had a relapse and had to go back into the hospital. I was at peace, ready to die. Instead, Jesus cut through my thoughts with the message, "No, it's not time to die—it's time to FOLLOW!"

Through my hospital stay, I finally recognized how much I was living as my own "savior." I depended on my strength and understanding instead of listening to, trusting, and following my Creator Jesus.

As I recovered from the internal bleeding, I made prayerful, intentional changes in my focus, priorities, and lifestyle. I practiced rejecting the my-way-highway and chose Jesus' Word, will, way, and time. My physical stress-related problems resolved, and our family became healthier in relationship with each other and God. My choice to follow Jesus, to let Him be Lord of the small and big things in my life, showed me the difference between peace and life (His way) and stress and death (my way).

With Jesus as Lord of my life and His Holy Spirit guiding me, I experience life as a new creation—joy beyond circumstances, peace amidst chaos, and possibilities beyond human comprehension and ability. My shoulders are unburdened as I roll my problems and concerns into the hands of my Creator. My stress evaporates as hope replaces despair, and I remember how God has brought family members and me through past trials. He gives me purpose, direction, wisdom, and all I need—when I ask Him and trust Him in the results.

I am thrilled to see God touch, heal, restore, and free hurting people, and I am honored to be a part of the process.

SECTION 1
DO YOU KNOW?

CHAPTER 38

You Are In A Battle: Which Side Will You Serve?

Everyone has wounds from life. Self-inflicted injuries and wounds from others lead to lies that we accept and live. Your spirit can be burdened, wounded, and restrained, just like your emotions, mind, and body. There are remarkable similarities in the symptoms that originate from physical causes, non-physical hurts, spiritual lies, wounds, and willful disobedience against our Creator.

Here is a list of common symptoms that result from mental and emotional wounds compared with spiritual injury and willful sin. Causes can be corrected, symptoms ended, and wounds can be healed when you address the source. Many of the symptoms are the same but people tend to treat mental, emotional, and physical symptoms through medical, mental, or medication therapy without addressing spiritual and post-trauma conditions and needs. That wastes money, time, and effort, and results in discouragement and hopelessness. Be aware of possible origins of your pain. God often uses discomforts to get our attention. Heal and correct the origins of the injury or problem.

Effects of Abuse and Trauma:	Effects of Sin or Spiritual Oppression:
Distrust of God and people	Distrust of God and people
Persistent feelings of secrecy, guilt, shame	Persistent feelings of secrecy, guilt, shame
Vague, confused, insecure identity	Vague, confused, insecure identity
Difficulty with relationships, unhealthy boundaries, driven, defensive	Difficulty with relationships, my-way-highway, pride, unhealthy boundaries, lazy, unteachable
Fragmented lifestyle—memory loss, disorganized, hard to keep a schedule, etc.	Fragmented lifestyle—procrastination, disorganized, hard to keep a schedule, etc.
Survival approach to life—unaware of options, shame, "I don't deserve" good things	Believed lies hinder release from bondage— "God can't," "God won't," "I'm too far gone"
Insecure or Poor self-worth	Insecure or Poor self-worth
Self-persecution, blame others	Pride, blame others, entitlement, self-centered
Victim mentality	Victim mentality
Confused—unaware of truth or it is colored by past wounds, lies, and pride	Confused—unaware of truth or it is colored by past wounds, lies, and pride
Destructive lifestyle	Destructive lifestyle to self and others
Nightmares, flashbacks, triggers	Addictions, abusive talk
Inappropriate threat reactions, secrecy	Manipulation, cover-up, secrecy
Exaggerated emotional responses	Exaggerated emotional responses

Worry, anxiety, persistent fears	Worry, anxiety, persistent fears
Depression	Depression
Physical pain and symptoms—fatigue, multiple and ongoing diagnoses, headaches, GI problems, etc.	Physical pain and symptoms—fatigue, multiple and ongoing diagnoses, headaches, GI problems, etc.
Sleeping and eating disorders	Sleeping and eating disorders

Our medical system treats symptoms and identified causes. But if symptoms continue, consider invisible contributors. Unconfessed sin (known or unknown) keeps us vulnerable to lies, enemy attacks, and growing bondage. In His Word, our Creator tells us that "the wages of sin is death."[53] Why would we ignore the warnings of our Maker? We should seek Him first for healing, not last or never. Healing occurs when we confess our disobedience, hurts, and heartaches to Jesus and seek help from caring, safe, God-honoring others.[54] We need accountability, support, prayer, and training to replace sin with godly thinking, choosing, and living.

> "There is no neutral ground in the universe. Every square inch, every split second, is claimed by God and counter-claimed by Satan." C. S. LEWIS

Do you know you are in a battle? You have seen the contest between good and evil in the news and your choices. Your heart, mind, body, and spirit experience signs of the battle—see the above list of sin and spiritual oppression symptoms. Jesus has won the war, but we still fight the battles in His strength, Word, and way.

Satan is a powerful, dangerous, deceptive spiritual-being who does all he can to tempt you away from God. Cast out of heaven because of his pride and rebellion against God, Satan has supernatural abilities, but he is nothing compared to God's almighty power. Since Satan has no power against God, he seeks to mislead and attack the people of God. Because love must be a choice, God allows each person to choose where they will place their loyalty and trust. There are only two eternal teams. You are on one of them the minute you are born. Is that the team you want? God wants you on His side and in His family.

Satan is a created, powerful, defeated, evil spiritual being, commanding many disobedient spiritual beings (demons or fallen angels). All of them are subject to the full power and authority of Jesus.[55] Satan's messages (his voice) contain lies about God, about who God made you to be (your God-given identity), and your purpose (your calling). Satan wants to steal your mind, kill the truth and your hope, and destroy your joy and potential.[56] Satan can have power over you *only if you allow it.* You can change that by accepting Jesus' victory and Lordship over all of you—your thoughts, words, and choices.

Some people think the spiritual battle is an arm-wrestling contest between equals. Wrong! A simple analogy would be to compare the oceans of the world (God) with a teaspoon of hydrochloric acid (Satan). Satan's evil purpose is to turn people away from the Creator God and control their minds and hearts. He prowls the earth enticing, attacking, and deceiving people.

Photo by frank mckenna on Unsplash

Picture yourself sitting on the beach, away from the water, lounging in the sun. You feel the warmth of the sun's ray, the cool breeze, and the sand between your toes. You know God is near (the ocean) because you are vaguely aware of the sound of the waves lapping on the sand. Without knowing it, that teaspoon of acid (Satan) comes up behind you and splashes on your shoulder. How does that feel?

In pain, you jump up. Maybe you wrongly blame the sun for your burns.

Where do you go for relief? If you run up the beach, away from the ocean, what happens to the acid on your skin? Running away from God isolates you and makes you more vulnerable to the pain, destruction, and Satan's control.

What happens if you decide to run into the ocean? As you go deeper into the water, your skin cools from the cleansing and healing saltwater. The acid is diluted until it's completely gone.

If you run into the ocean (God), the acid (Satan) is overcome and washed away. If you only walk into the water up to shoulder level, the acid can still burn you. However, if you immerse yourself and dive deep into the ocean, the acid cannot reach you. It neutralizes the instant it comes in contact with the sea. Immerse deeply in the ocean of Jesus' saving grace, the Holy Spirit, God's Word, will, and way. Then, the damaging acid of Satan has no power over you or God's blessing, protection, provision, and purpose in your life.

᧞᧞ ᧞᧞ ᧞᧞ ᧞᧞ ᧞᧞

How often do you think about what motivates and controls you? Without examination, we stay busy—Being Under Satan's Yoke. We are under the control of what we think about most frequently— loss (past or future), what we love most (money, position, health), or what we fear (death, not being needed, being alone, or turning off our devices).

What you *think about most* is your god, your master. If all you are and all you have belongs to our Lord Jesus, you live out the purpose for which you were created. As a Christian, you surrender control of your motives, thoughts, words, choices, and actions to Jesus, and He will lead you to more purpose and joy than you can imagine.[57] Fear disappears.[58] Who or what do you want controlling you?

The Gospel of John teaches that Jesus wants you to have a close relationship with God. And He paid the price for you to have a relationship like He has always had with God, His

Father—the ideal caring, protective, nurturing Perfect Parent with His Child. Jesus is the only Way to a relationship with God, our Father. His love cannot be earned—it is a gift. You can reject Him, but He is always with you, waiting to be your Provider, Protector, Guide, Healer, and Friend. He fights for, cares for, and blesses His children and punishes the wicked.

In his letters to the Romans and Corinthians, Paul teaches that Jesus cleanses, heals, forgives, and frees you from bondage (sin) if you let Him. He loves you and cares for the details of your life. His Holy Spirit comforts you, trains you for your good, transforms you, and gifts you with abilities to live out God's purpose and plan for you. God provides everything you need for life. Do you want to be responsible for all of that?

Psalm 139:13-16 tells us that God has planned our lives before His creation of the world. He knows paths of our daily lives. Only He can protect and sustain us through unknown dangers and prepare us for unforeseen opportunities.

If you decide you want to direct and drive your life, you are on your own. You determine Jesus is your judge instead of your Savior. Is that what you want? Don't miss out on the peace, joy, assurance, hope, and wonder of knowing God as your Creator and experiencing all He has prepared for you as promised in Ephesians 2:10.

SECTION 2
FOOD FOR THOUGHT

CHAPTER 39

Your Life-Train: Who Controls Your Life Train?

What powers your life train? What is your compass, your plumb line for decision-making, and joyful living? Do you have the power and stability of facts guiding your responses, or do your emotions rule your reactions and life?

Fact

Facts show the driver, the engineer of your life train, realistic options, motives, and appropriate choices. Facts provide direction and point to steps in achieving desired goals. Jesus is the only trustworthy engineer—He alone knows the best path for your life because He is The Way, The Truth, and The Life.[59] Who drives your life train? The wrong driver could go the wrong way. If you drive your life train, you will get lost, break down, derail your purpose, and forfeit joy in the journey.

Surrender your life train to the Master Engineer, Jesus. He has the map and compass for your life and knows how to take care of and repair your train. Jesus knows how to avoid traps in life and lead you to the greatest joys. He has the wisdom, strength, and power to get you through the toughest trials of life. Would you rather fumble around in the dark, tripping, getting injured, and wasting time? Or follow the One who has the light and the map. Now we will build on the concepts presented previously.

Based on God's Word, will, way, and time, your facts engine (driven by engineer Jesus) powers you up steep hills, around or through obstacles, brakes for control down the mountain, and keeps you on track toward your purpose and blessings. With multiple wheels, your fact engine connects solidly to the tracks and traction of God's Word, objective reality, and wise choices. The fact engine lights realistic options and direction and leads the boxcar of faith and the caboose of feelings. If the feeling caboose leads, your life train is going backward without a competent driver, light, or control. Your life derails quickly into a crumpled catastrophe.

> *"For I know the plans that I have for you," declares the LORD, "plans for welfare and not for calamity to give you a future and a hope. Then you will call upon Me and come and pray to Me, And I will listen to you. You will seek Me and find [Me] when you search for Me with all your heart."*
> *Jeremiah 29:11-13 NASB*

Jesus knows—we don't know—the plans He has for you and me. Depend on yourself, and you are limited to your strength, understanding, ability, and endurance. Plug into the Source of wisdom, power, peace, and potential, and there is much beyond what you can attain on your own. Get off the my-way-highway; it leads to destruction. Accept Jesus as your Engineer and receive joy, peace, blessing, and all you need for the good and bad times of life.

"For by grace you have been saved through faith;
and that not of yourselves, [it is] the gift of God;
not as a result of works, so that no one may boast.
For we are His workmanship, created in
Christ Jesus for good works, which God prepared
beforehand so that we would walk in them."
Ephesians 2:8-10 NASB

Faith

Faith in your Creator strongly and positively impacts your life train. How effectively and positively your life train operates depends on where you put your faith. Do you trust your Creator as much as you trust elements of daily life?

Think of all the things you automatically trust:

- A breath of fresh air
- The sun rising in the morning
- Electricity when you flip a switch
- Mail delivered on time to pay a bill
- Transportation to get you to your destination

All the manmade things we trust every day can and have failed, but God's sufficiency does not fail. Where is your focus? On what or in whom do you rely? If you put faith in money, material things, position, yourself, or other people, you limit your life, focus, and function. However, when you trust your Creator God Almighty, your purpose and life have potential beyond your strength, understanding, and ability.

Faith results in hope. Hope in God is not a wish—hope is a promise you can count on through faith in your Engineer Jesus. Faith fuels the facts of Jesus' promises to get you through and show you great and mighty things. Faith allows hope to overshadow facts. Hope gives you and me the ability to imagine possibilities beyond visible facts. Hope builds confidence in our Creator beyond human capacity, control, and understanding. Have you seen any miracles? I have experienced many situations where God accomplished what seemed impossible through human rationale, strength, finances, knowledge, or time.

Communication with your driver, engineer Jesus, through prayer, allows you to know where He is leading and how to prepare. It means listening and speaking. Reading God's Word and praying keeps you secure on sturdy rails and off the my-way-highway. Through faith, you trust and experience the sufficiency and reliability of your Lord Jesus. You also share joy and connection with others on the journey.

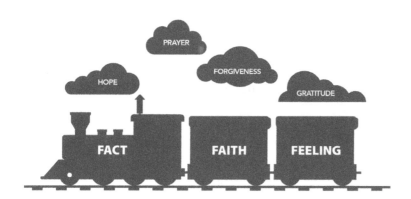

Feeling

Feelings enhance and cement our perspectives but have no compass or basis in reality without facts. When feelings lead, it is easy to misunderstand and cause deep wounds to yourself and others. Don't let your feelings drive your actions or control your thinking. If emotions control you, disaster follows.

One of the best ways to balance and guide your emotions is with an attitude of gratitude. Gratitude turns your emotions and your focus from self to the Source of all you need for life. In every difficult situation, failed expectation, or shattered dream, your mental and physical health improve when you focus on the good things you have instead of holding onto past or current pain.

Forgiving is not forgetting

Another crucial ingredient to improve your emotional state is to forgive others. Forgiving is nearly impossible for people to do in their will and strength. Deep wounds of heart, mind, and spirit will fester and grow, poisoning you with bitterness, resentment, fuming anger, or desire for vengeance when you don't forgive.

Forgiving is not forgetting. It is not intuitive or easy, but you are the one who benefits from your choice to forgive. When you ask Jesus for the ability to forgive, you release your pain and anger into the hands of God. The wound you sustained, though not forgotten, will fade. New life and healing come as the pain moves into the past where it belongs.

Forgiving is sacrificial. Jesus demonstrated this on the cross when He said, "Father, forgive them for they do not know what they do."[60] People rejecting God betrayed, abandoned, brutalized, and nailed Him to the cross.

Forgiving cleanses, heals, and frees your heart, mind, spirit, and body and puts others into the hands of God.

For physical, mental, emotional, and spiritual health:

- Be sure God's Word and facts lead your life train, thinking, and decision-making.[61]
- Let faith fuel your facts and generate hope so you can be open to God's plan and power.[62]
- Stay in close communication with your Lord and engineer, Jesus, through prayer rooted in God's Word and faith.[63]
- Feelings are not leadership qualified.[64]
- An attitude of gratitude balances your feelings with facts, takes your eyes off of self, refocuses on your blessings and the Giver, and changes you from victim to victor.[65]
- Forgive to remove poisonous bitterness, resentment, victimization, anger, and vengeance that harms only

you. Forgiving in Jesus' power puts your pain, anger, and the other person in His hands.[66]

Jesus commanded us to forgive and be forgiven in that order.[67] If we do not forgive, how can we be forgiven? After His teaching on prayer, Jesus spoke about forgiveness in Matthew 6:14-15. Forgiving is vital for our well-being now and in eternity.

❧ ❧ ❧ ❧ ❧

It is vital to fully release all your pain, anger, and strong feelings to the Lord for effective repentance. We cannot reject what we continue to hold on to, in part or in full.

What does it mean to release to the Lord?

Release is a choice. Don't wait until you want to release and forgive. You probably won't desire to forgive someone who hurt you deeply. Our motives and weakness hinder forgiving. We tend to take back what we release. We must have God's help and strength. Our responsibility is to choose to forgive and release our pain, anger, and desire for vengeance into God's perfect judgment. Then, allow God to deal with the person who caused the injury. As long as you hold on to your hurts, you suffer from festering anger, bitterness, resentment, victim-ization, and more. The target of your unforgiveness remains unaffected. Just as pressure and infection increase in an abscess, the person harboring unforgiveness becomes poisoned and robbed of God's joy, freedom, healing, and potential.

Release is active. We can pray, "O Lord, take my sin, take my pain, relieve me!" God is gracious, merciful, and loving, but He may want to teach you something. Release requires a giver and a receiver—a connection. God wants you to come to Him, to make a choice and effort to seek Him—to put your pain, problem, wound, or another person into His hands.

Release has many forms. It is easy to release a pen or object into someone's open hand. We can toss it in a quick, easy, hot-potato-type transfer or get the receiver's attention and confirm the reception. When praying, do you fling your cares and needs toward Jesus as you run past Him? Do you release all of the concern to Him or do you hold on to bits and pieces? Do you spend time with Jesus, search the Scriptures, and ask Him to show you how to release? Do you ask Him for what He will give you in return as you release and forgive your offenders?

Whom do you need to forgive or ask to forgive you?

GOD came to Earth

In Jesus, the final, perfect Passover Lamb, the Great I AM, did not come to Earth to help bad people become good. He came to bring spiritually and eternally dead people to life![68] No matter how good we are, we disobey God and need the Lord Jesus Christ to be our Savior.

When people read John 3:16, we tend to focus on our importance instead of the unimaginable sacrifice of God as both Father and Son. Yes, He loves us. He paid our legal and relational debt for sin, which is death. Our focus needs to be on Jesus. Our incomprehensibly merciful and gracious Savior, Lord, and King gave His life to draw us close to Him in relationship and for eternity.

For years, around Christmastime, Paul Harvey would read the story, *The Man and the Birds,* on his radio program. Here is the essence of that story. What does it say to you?

The Man and the Birds

There was a kind man. He was generous to his family and upright in his dealings with other men. But he was just not able to believe the incarnation story the Bible told about and that he heard at Christmas, about

God coming to Earth as a man to show us His love and how to live. It didn't make sense to him, and he was too honest to pretend otherwise.

"I am truly sorry," he told his wife, "but I am not going to church with you this Christmas Eve. I would much rather stay home." Shortly after his wife and children drove away, snow began to fall. He went to the window to watch the flurries swirling about. Then he sat down by the fireside and began to read his newspaper.

Soon he was startled by a thudding sound and then another and another. He thought, "Somebody must be throwing snowballs against the living room window." When he went to the front door to investigate, he found a flock of birds huddled miserably in the snow. They had been caught in the storm and, in desperate search for shelter, had tried to fly through his front window.

He couldn't let the poor creatures lie there and freeze. He felt he had to do something. He remembered the barn where his children stabled their pony. That would provide a warm, cozy shelter for these birds and there would be plenty for them to eat—if he could just direct the birds to it.

He put on his coat and boots and tramped through the deep snow to the barn. He opened the doors wide and turned on the lights, but the birds would not come in out of the raging storm. He thought food would entice them to enter the protection and warmth of the barn. He sprinkled breadcrumbs on the snow, making a trail to the open doorway. But the birds ignored the breadcrumbs and  continued to flop around helplessly in the snowstorm. He tried catching them. He tried shooing them. He tried chasing them into the barn by walking around them and waving his arms. Instead of moving toward the refuge awaiting them, they scattered in every direction, away from the warm, lighted barn.

Any move he made tended to frighten and confuse them. They would not follow or be led.

Then the man realized that they were afraid of him. "To them," he reasoned, "I am a huge, strange, terrifying creature. If only I could think of some way to let them know that I offer what they need, and they can trust me. But how? If only I could be a bird," he thought, "and could mingle with them and speak their language, I could tell them not to be afraid. I could show them the way to the safe, warm, food-filled barn. If only I were one of them, they could see, hear, understand, and live."

At that moment, the church bells began to ring. The sound reached the man's ears above the sound of the wind and he stood listening to the bells peal "O Come, All Ye Faithful." Listening to the bells sounding out the glad tidings of Christmas, he suddenly understood why there was Christmas and he sank to his knees in the snow.[69]

"For God did not send the Son into the world to judge the world, but that the world might be saved through Him. John 3:17 NASB

SECTION 3

LET'S DO THIS!

CHAPTER 40

Choose This Day: Start Your Healing and New Life Now!

Every possible sin can be forgiven if you earnestly, honestly, completely turn from that evil. It may take time, and it certainly takes commitment to say *no* to the temptation every time, but in God's strength, you will be victorious. Ask your Creator to forgive you. Follow Jesus as Savior and Lord of your life. The only unforgivable sin is when *you refuse* to turn from evil, *reject* God's forgiveness, and *resist* payment for your offense that Jesus provided in His death on the cross. If you choose to push God away, He will honor your choice—but He will be available until you die if you decide to turn toward Him and accept rescue from eternal hell.

If you want to *live* in the perfect care, protection, provision, fulfillment, and blessing of your Creator, you can do that now. You don't need to know anything about Jesus or Christianity; you need to *want* to learn the truth about your identity, purpose, and eternity. You must desire to be and see all that God, the Father, Son, and Holy Spirit plans for you. Your relationship with our Creator is a journey. It takes time to learn about our Lord and grow in truth, trust, and dependence on Him. It is vital to find and learn from people who live out God's Word in their relationships, choices, and lives.

Start New Life Now!

1. Do you want abundant life? Are you willing to give up your old way of living, thinking, and choosing? Will you accept the invitation, life change, and the enormous potential Jesus offers when He says, "Follow Me"?[70] The Christian life is not pain-free. In some ways, living for Jesus will be more challenging. You may experience ridicule and rejection by people you thought were your friends. You will say "no" to the enticing but harmful activities that gave temporary pleasure in the past. Your life will change. The internal peace, joy, rest, and blessing you receive will be well worth all of the difficult God-honoring choices you make.

2. Be honest. You have been selfish, hurt others, and hurt yourself in multiple ways. We all have. Recognize that your way doesn't work. You disobeyed the God who made you, loves you, and died to buy you back. Humans make terrible mistakes because we are sinners.[71] The only One who can save you and me from a horrible eternity is Jesus, the perfect Passover Lamb, the only Son of God, the Creator of all.[72]

3. Believe Jesus died a torturous death on a cross to pay for your disobedience and rejection of Him. History and witnesses verify Jesus' death and resurrection.[73]

4. Be sorry for hurting the heart of God and for hurting others. Repent, which means to do an about-face. Turn away from those thoughts, choices, and activities that dishonor God.[74]

5. Ask Jesus to forgive you and be your personal Lord and Savior. Ask Him to lead you in His way. Make Jesus Lord of your life. Ask Him to direct your thoughts, emotions, words, and actions.[75]

6. Grow in the grace and knowledge of Jesus, the Messiah.[76] Being a Christian is not just a label, a one-time event, or religion. Accepting Jesus Christ as your Lord and Savior is not the end. It is the beginning of a life-long

change and journey. Being a Christian means you are a new creation, Christ-like, and in relationship with your Creator. This new relationship involves listening, speaking, and growing together. People are fallible and will disappoint, break promises, and let you down. However, His Holy Spirit is with you at all times. As you learn His true identity, you understand Jesus can and will keep His promises.[77] He is always trustworthy. Get to know Him!

7. Keep up the relationship! Relationship means communication, so listen to God. Read the Bible (Basic Instructions Before Leaving Earth) daily. Talk to God through prayer throughout your day. Surround yourself with Christians who honor God and act like Jesus. Find a church that teaches the full Word of God. Look over the Resource list to see what might help you regularly grow.[78]

Stop, Drop, and Pray (S-D-P)

Doesn't it sometimes feel like you are on fire in the chaos of life? Everyone pulls you in a different direction. There is never enough time, energy, or rest. What about when you or those you love are in a financial, relational, or health crisis? That's the time to S-D-P.

STOP:
- Plug into the Source of strength, wisdom, provision, protection, and direction.
- Review the previous stress management tools (B-M-W; O-C-A).
- Recognize your Creator. He made you, knows your name, your days, your steps. He is with you, and He can ease your way if you let Him.

DROP:
- Drop to your knees—mentally and physically. Fall into Father God's almighty arms.

- Recognize that you are not alone. He is the Daddy; you are the child.
- Release your problems, concerns, and condition to your Maker's greater power and care.

PRAY:
- Communicate with the One Triune God in heaven
- Communication = speak and listen.
- Speak your concerns silently or out loud.
- Look for His promises in the Bible.
- Read God's Word to listen and learn His will and way.
- Pray with your spouse, family, and friends.
- When crises happen, pray to Almighty God first, not last!
- Trust the outcome to Him—beyond your understanding and expectations

Just as children learn to stop, drop, and roll if their clothes catch on fire, we, too, should stop, drop, and pray to put out the fires of chaos, confusion, and temptation that steal our joy and threaten our lives. Make a habit of praying with your family. Spend daily time with your Creator and Lord by reading the Bible, God's Word. Pour out your heart to Him in prayer. Look for and thank Him for His answers.

SECTION 4
TRAIN TO MAINTAIN

CHAPTER 41

Improve Your Walk: How is Your Spirit Exercise?

To train and improve your walk with God, read His Word, the Bible. Surround yourself with people who show they love and honor Jesus in their talk, choices, and relationships. Join a Bible study and learn to apply God's Word to your life. Grow in a personal relationship with our Lord Jesus.

A relationship starts with learning about another person, which takes time. Relationships require communication—listening and speaking (often best in that order). We listen to God by reading and studying His Word, the Bible. We talk to the Lord in prayer. With any communication, it is essential to know to whom you are speaking.

When you pray, use God's identifying characteristics and titles, such as "God Almighty," "Savior," "Great I AM," "Creator," "King of Kings and Lord of Lords," "Yeshua ha Mashiach." Build a habit of learning the true identity and marvelous attributes of our Creator God. Pray to Him by name as you savor and explore His distinctiveness and love. Check out the Resources at the end of this book and enjoy your journey with Jesus!

Live It! The Daily 7 R's

The following is a guide for prayer. Certain elements are important to remember before you add your specifics. You might want to read the Scripture references, personalize those verses, and share your heart with God in your own words. Prayer is talking to God. Be yourself.

The 7 Rs Daily Prayer Guide:
- **Recognize** — 2 Corinthians 13:5, Psalm 119:59-60
  - o The problem: Pain, fear, or something else.
  - o God and His power: Bring all to Jesus—He can handle it all.
- **Release** — Psalm 55:22-23; Philippians 4:6-7
  - o Submit yourself, desires, and control into Jesus perfect care – James 4:7-8
  - o Actively give events and people to Jesus. Ask Him to help you to not take it back.
- **Repent** – 1 John 1:9; 2 Chronicles 7:14-15
  - o Confess accepted lies, sin, bondage
  - o Confess sinful influences and effects on yourself and others
  - o Actively turn away from sin and temptation
- **Renounce** — 2 Corinthians 4:1-2; Proverbs 28:13
  - o Exposure to evil—past, present, future
  - o Evil thoughts, images, choices, actions in your life
  - o The lies, sin, demonic influence, control, contracts, agreements
- **Refuse** — 1 Thessalonians 5:21-24; Ephesians 6:13; 1 Corinthians 10:13
  - o Immediately reject lies, sin; know and stand on Jesus' victory over sin, death, and Satan
  - o Constantly refuse junk mail (the voices and messages of the flesh, the world, the enemy)
- **Reclaim** God's best for you — Genesis 50:20; Colossians 1:10
  - o You can't claim, or live out God's best for you if you don't know God's promises
  - o Ask, receive, and live out the fullness of God's plan for you
- **Replace** — Matthew 12: 43-45; Ephesians 1:18-21

 o Lies with the Truth
 o Ask for God's replacement, restoration, protection, blessing, wisdom, and direction

Live It! 4x4 Spiritual First Aid Kit

Temptation or pressures often catch you off guard. Under stress or strong emotion, it is hard to imagine how to avoid reacting. You need a spiritual first aid kit when you feel depressed, attacked, worthless, overwhelmed, or far from God to help you process negative messages, repeating lies, or ungodly images that enter your mind.

This 4x4 Healing First Aid Kit helps. Keep it handy. Use these tools when you are not pressured, so they will be your default when you need them.

- For 15 to 30 minutes, read God's Word first thing in the morning and before bed to set your thoughts, priorities, dreams, and day, and to protect your heart and mind.
- Journal your feelings and thoughts. Keep a prayer journal of how God works in your life.
- Give your concerns to Jesus. Read scripture. Pray and ask for His Truth to replace lies. Write lies and the corresponding truth on index cards or in a small notebook. Whenever a lie or negative message comes up, refute it immediately with the truth you have written.
- Leave these truth reminders where you will run into them frequently—in your car, bedroom, bathroom, kitchen, purse, wallet, etc.
- On index cards or in your journal, write scripture verses in "I" messages: "I know ___, I am ___, I choose ___." Put your name into the scriptures where appropriate. If you are not sure, ask God, study the passage with a pastor or other knowledgeable person.
- Listen to restful, uplifting Christian music. Keep your favorites handy to listen to when you go to bed, wake up, feel discouraged, or stressed.

- Have a list of at least five people you can call for support and prayer. Call the numbers on your list until you talk to a person!

Key Points and Summary

- S-D-P (Stop, Drop, and Pray) regularly and with your spouse and family to prioritize your day and prevent the fires of chaos and enemy attack.
- Master your time, activities, money, and technology. Don't allow them to enslave you. Are you overwhelmed, sidetracked, and bogged down by being B-U-S-Y: Being Under Satan's Yoke?
- Satan is not equal to God. He is a created being under the sovereign control of Almighty God. Satan has no power over you when you accept Jesus as Lord and Savior. (Read James 4:7-8)
- Accept Jesus' gift of life and sacrifice. You cannot earn your way to eternal heaven with good deeds. Only the Son of God, the perfect Passover Lamb, could pay the price of sin in His death and resurrection. Make Him your Lord and Savior.

I pray you intimately know *The Heart of Healing*, which is our Savior, Healer, and Lord, Jesus the Messiah. Be blessed!

I pray that your hearts will be flooded with light so that you can understand the confident hope He has given to those He called—His holy people who are His rich and glorious inheritance. I also pray that you will understand the incredible greatness of God's power for us who believe Him. This is the same mighty power that raised Christ from the dead and seated Him in the place of honor at God's right hand in the heavenly realms.
Ephesians 1:18-20 NLT

A FINAL NOTE TO THE READER

I hope and pray you found the information presented in *The Heart of Healing* useful as a first step in assessing and caring for common complaints. Each person benefits from a thorough evaluation and individualized care if pain and problems do not resolve with initial basic care. Don't settle—be your very best!

Check out the brief videos and specific online courses covering topics from this book at 4x4Healing.com.

I'd love to hear from you. Contact me at Bonnie@4x4Healing.com with your questions.

A FINAL NOTE TO HEALTH CARE PROVIDERS

If medical professions exist to resolve pathology, it is inconsistent to extensively attend to physical pain, dysfunction, and symptoms without recognizing and attending to the non-physical contributors to those maladies. Likewise, it is counterproductive for those promoting mental, emotional, and spiritual health to ignore the powerful language and impact of the physical body.

Clinical training instills a take-charge attitude, which is helpful and harmful. Only when the patient feels safe, heard, respected, and valued can they receive the provider's perspective of confidence and leadership. Sensitive care is critical for successful patient care, no matter the complexity or severity of the physical, emotional, mental, or spiritual wounds. Patient satisfaction and confidence improve when you give each patient time, a listening ear and heart, and control in their health care as you offer options and guide treatment.

We are trained to fix things—to focus on and press toward a goal through our desire to see patient improvement, achieve our patient's hopes, and satisfy insurance payers protocol. It is more important to meet each patient where he or she is in the healing journey. Five minutes of quality listening is a potent step to total healing.

Listen carefully to the patient—build trust through LOVE

- Listen carefully to the heart, mind, spirit, and body.
- Observe body language, non-verbal communication, and message continuity.
- Validate the patient's feelings, which are real no matter the circumstances.
- Engage and encourage patient participation in the goal development and plan of care.

Be aware of visible and invisible sources of pain or problems.

- Pay attention to physical pain and symptoms caused by pathology or expressions of deep internal wounds, lies, and fears.
- Be sensitive to emotional (heart) wounds, fear, despair.
- Discern mental contributors like lies, overwhelming trauma, denial.
- Consider spiritual experiences that distort true identity and crush hope.
- Share this book and ask your patients what touched them, what helped, or what made them uncomfortable.

What we believe is what we live.

Retrain and replace unhealthy mental, emotional, and physical reactions with positive, healthy responses.

For more detailed information, check out the free previews of Provider online courses, including "Sensitive Care for Trauma Survivors" at 4x4Healing.com.

APPENDICES

APPENDIX

Active Relaxation

Active Relaxation is the awareness and ability to turn off muscle tension intentionally. You learn to identify habitual, stress-induced, and specific muscle tension and volitionally relax those muscles.

Write down everything going through your head. Like a cloud of gnats buzzing around your head, "to-dos" and mental messages can plague you. Swat those gnats onto paper! Get all your thoughts and feelings out on paper. Leave them there until you are well-rested, can think clearly, and can sort out lies and truths with wise, caring others.

As you write down all your churning thoughts and feelings, B-M-W to quiet your brain and body. Check out my website—4x4Healing.com—for information and helps on the Breathe-Melt-Wiggle tool.

When you have left everything on paper, melt with every breath you exhale—sink deeper and deeper into the mattress or chair. Slowly tense your muscles and then let go, from the top of your head to the tips of your toes—sink deeply into the bed. Continue practicing this "active relaxation" to train your body and your mind to let go. Use this skill to manage stress during your active day.

Are your feet cold? Get socks or microwavable booties to warm your feet and your bed. Is there a mild or major discomfort that you can remedy? It is surprising how fast you can relax and sleep when you are cozy and comfortable.

APPENDIX

Active vs. Passive Stretching

My guess is you know the difference between active and passive in general. Let's apply that to stretching.

Active stretching uses the muscles around that joint to stretch the tissues. In other words, the muscles that control the joint should do the stretching and strengthening around that joint. It's all about muscle balance and control—we want the muscles around your spine, knee, shoulder, and each joint to do the stretching, strengthening, and build stability and control in the process.

Passive stretching, on the other hand, is stretching using external force. So, what does passive stretching look like? Look around you. Passive stretching is most common because people naturally use their strong muscles to do work that their weak muscles can't do. When you passively stretch, you use one arm to pull on your neck, leg, or the other arm. Do you use that arm to move and control those joints? No—you have just stretched, loosened, or destabilized those areas with external force. You think you are stretching your hamstrings (the back of your thigh) by sitting on the floor, leaning over, and touching your toes when, in reality, you are probably stretching your lower back or sacroiliac tissues. The weight of your upper body will pull on the weakest area. Your hamstring muscles are larger and stronger than your spinal muscles, so, without protecting your back, those smaller, weaker back tissues will give and be stretched. Your hamstrings won't be touched. The strong get stronger, and the weak get weaker. Active stretching protects the weak, vulnerable areas while specifically stretching tight tissues.

It's not what you do but more **how** you do it that counts. Want to stretch your hamstrings? Good. Lie on your back on the floor with a rolled bath towel (about 1.5-2.0 inches thick) under your back at the waist. With your legs straight, pull one bent knee toward your chest, until your hip is bent 90 degrees. Use only your leg strength—no hands!—to hold your thigh vertical, at 90-degrees. Keep your other leg straight, flat on the floor and your back against the rolled towel. Hold the 90-degree hip flexion position as you slowly straighten your knee as far as you can without moving your thigh. You probably cannot straighten your knee completely. In fact, your knee may be bent quite a bit. But if you have kept your hip bent at 90 degrees, you are effectively stretching your hamstrings—you are *actively* stretching! Your quadriceps muscles (on the front of your thigh) are getting stronger as they stretch the opposing hamstrings muscles, and these two muscle groups control your knee motion. Hold your stretch for 30 seconds and repeat three times on each leg. For best results, do this exercise at least three times per day until you can straighten your knee while holding your leg at 90-degrees of hip flexion for thirty seconds.

APPENDIX

Are Your Words Heard?

The tone of your voice and your facial expression register in the other person's brain much faster than the words you say. Subconscious messages from facial expressions are received as quickly as the time it takes for one brain cell to fire.[79]

As you speak, your tone of voice, facial expression, past experiences, and deep emotions subconsciously dictate the meaning of your words. More than your words, the person to whom you speak retains and reacts subconsciously—physically, mentally, and emotionally—to the powerful messages you telegraph through your face, body language, and tone of voice.

Your brain is pliant and has great potential for healing.

No matter what words you speak, the most influential, longest-lasting messages received by another person come from the tone of your voice, your facial expression, and body language, which filter through the other person's experience and deeply held beliefs.

Years of physical pain, emotional turmoil, and relational struggles easily overwhelm an essential fact: Your brain is pliant and has great potential for healing.[80] Connect with a caring, skilled professional and see how much better life can be!

APPENDIX
Fatigue and Negative Thought Progressions

If your mind reviews what happened during the day or churns over the demands of the future, your sleep will most likely be fitful, interrupted, and not restful. Rehashing past wounds or future possibilities leads to distorted perspectives. There is a pattern to these habits. Consider the following examples of common thought progressions:

You are concerned about what you said or did, what others think of you, or about unhealthy choices that your loved ones are making. You rehash the day, your words, your relationships, your feelings:

1. What should I or could I have done differently?
2. What if I…...?

Up to this point, your reflection and evaluation are healthy. It stops here with constructive answers—"I could have done or said this better by _____" or "I could not improve the situation—I need to pray." You are now able to let the issue go. If you continue ruminating over the past, the focus subtly shifts more and more to self:

1) "It's my fault," "I can't do anything right," "They don't like me," or "There is something wrong with me."

2) "I deserve better than this," "This shouldn't have happened to me," "Things will never get better," "This is not fair," "It's their fault."

3) You lose perspective in your isolated, self-focused thoughts. In your fatigue at night, you might not see clearly what you have control over and what you have no control over—they blend together.

4) Now, your feelings grow stronger. You assign blame for your actions to others or tell yourself you are responsible for others' choices and actions.

5) The negative thoughts and messages become exaggerated and prevalent. Unhealed internal wounds amplify negative perceptions and believed lies.

If you find yourself falling into this progression, journal and find caring support to help you prayerfully uncover lies and wounds so that you can heal.

APPENDIX

Headaches to Plantar Fasciitis

Head and Neck

Headaches can result from muscle tension, fatigue, caffeine, stress, smoke or air pollution, bright light, wearing glasses, blood pressure or vascular problems, past trauma, and more causes than we can list here. Headaches vary in intensity, frequency, and duration, occurring once or twice per year, lasting a few minutes to daily to hours.

A common source of headaches is poor postural alignment and muscle tension, as in the diagnosis of "texting neck," caused by prolonged poor head and neck posture while using hand-held technology. Another cause of neck pain is gradual loss of motion due to disuse.

The office door opened, and Mrs. Y, a 96-year-old woman, entered. Her brow was furrowed, and there was no smile on her face. I approached her cautiously to see how she was doing. This elderly lady respectfully and forcefully told me she was very unhappy about her stiff neck and could not turn her head, preventing her from swimming. A joy for most of her adult life had been her daily swim.

Mrs. Y had been told by her doctor to accept her limitation and be happy that she has had a good life at her age. She was not pleased. She wanted to return to swimming, and she wanted me to help her.

After completing her evaluation and listening to her history, I found that Mrs. Y had lost rotation in her neck gradually over time. She was only able to turn her head about ten degrees to each side. (Normal neck rotation is about 60-70 degrees to each side.) Subtle disuse over months and years caused joint stiffness and muscle degeneration. Mrs. Y was well motivated. She scheduled her treatments twice per week and performed her progressive IHP properly and consistently. Within six weeks, Mrs. Y was continuing to progress in her IHP and was back to swimming.

Look around as you go through your day. Observe the head, neck, and shoulder position of people around you. How do they habitually use their phones or computers, drive, do paperwork, etc.? Check your position and tune in to how those positions feel. Review proper posture and alignment, the foundation.

ACTIVITY

Put your fingers on your forehead and move the skin around. Is there any pain, or do you only feel the pressure of your fingers? Does the skin move easily, without pain, about half the width of your fingertip? That is the desirable norm, not only for your forehead but also for your scalp. Now, put your fingers on your head and move the muscles and skin of your scalp. Most often, your scalp tissues are less mobile and more tender than your forehead.

Ideally, your scalp will be as mobile as your forehead and not be sensitive or tender to massage. If you suffer headaches, listen to your body. Here are some simple but important things you can do to attend to your body and prevent headaches. You can use some or all of these techniques and in any order:

1) Correct your posture! This is the most important aspect for lasting improvement. Retract your chin backward toward your neck, and pull your shoulders down, out of your ears. Be consistent! Writing the reasons you want to

improve your posture (i.e., relieving pain, looking better, feeling better through the day, enhancing breathing and digestion, preventing headaches and arthritis) will remind you to practice and keeps you motivated. Review the information about proper posture and alignment. Remember, proper posture is the foundation of position and movement. Excellent alignment prevents pain and degenerative changes.

2) Rest! Remember that rest is more than just sleeping, so get all the benefits of rest or get appropriate help.

3) Actively relax your muscles, gently tuck your chin, and pull your shoulders down toward your feet. Where are you holding tension? Put pressure on those tight areas and tighten those muscles. Feel the difference between the tense and relaxed state of the muscles. Use the red dots to remind you to B-M-W and actively relax areas where you hold tension habitually.

4) Gently massage all over your head, neck, and ears. If you wear glasses, take them off and massage around your ears and temples. If you feel pain when you massage your scalp or the base of your skull, use ice properly, and gently massage your scalp and the base of your neck until the pain ceases.

5) Use ice packs properly, without causing frostbite, to stop muscle spasm and relieve pain.

Shoulder Rotation

Poor posture affects your shoulders. The muscles supporting your shoulder joint, the rotator cuff, cannot function well in poor alignment. The length and strength balance of connective tissues (ligaments, tendons, and soft tissues, including muscle) is critical for lasting joint function. Misalignment will cause shoulder pain, limitation, and a demanding rehabilitation. "Set" your triangle of stability (as instructed in the postural information presented earlier), and the glitch and discomfort will probably cease.

In 2006, I threw a bale of hay, and my right hand became entangled in the bailing twine. I tore my right rotator cuff. The surgical repair was extensive. After healing, I couldn't put my hand behind my back. I found that I could barely reach my right hand behind my right leg. I was shocked at how much motion I had lost.

I did everything a physical therapist should do. Nothing seemed to work until I patiently and consistently worked on the exercise pictured here. Little by little, over six months, I asked my fingers to climb up my back toward my left hand that was up and over my head, reaching down my back. I didn't pull my hand up but worked the back of my right hand up my spine, keeping my right elbow forward. I just asked my muscles and joints to go a little farther each time—staying under the point of "bad pain" but feeling the work and stretch. As I did this exercise consistently, I was able to regain full motion and rotator cuff strength. The goal is to **actively** touch fingertips without using external force—like using a towel or rope—to pull the hands together. I continue to "SET" my core stabilizers and check this ability monthly. When I can't touch fingertips easily, I get back on the exercise.

Arms and Hands

In decades past, students took copious notes by hand. We used typewriters that supplied arduous hand and finger workouts. Letters were written by hand, and students were encouraged to develop beautiful handwriting. Today, we have the blessings of light touch computer keyboards and swipe phone texting. Current arm and hand weakness result in over-use problems.

Piano players build up their hand and forearm strength and endurance over the years by practicing and adapting to complex and taxing finger work demands. Computers are part of life at work and home. Carpal tunnel and other over-use syndromes can develop when people get into computer jobs that demand long hours of finger dexterity and endurance without prior muscle training over time. Necessary longhand writing can result in shoulder, arm, and hand fatigue and pain. In many cases, both of these problems can be resolved completely without surgery.

Our daughter was studying for a work-related license and was taking notes by hand for hours. She experienced pain in her neck, upper back, shoulders, arms, and hands—much more severely on the dominant, writing side. Why did she have symptoms in both shoulders and arms? As she was studying and writing, she was supporting her tired body on her arms. Her pain resolved with three or four treatments, appropriate use of numbing cold, and consistent IHP.

Numbness and tingling in your arms and hands can frequently come from shoulder girdle tightness. Nerve impingement can also occur at your neck and any place along your arms and hands. In my experience, the vast majority of upper extremity numbness and tingling resolves well by treating and correcting shoulder girdle muscle imbalance.

"Set" your shoulders *before* moving your arms. Use both arms equally. What you do with one side of your body, do with the other side whenever possible, just like in the movie, *Karate Kid*.

When I brush my horses, I use both arms equally to brush from head to tail on one side, and then I do the same on the other side. My arms work to the right and the left equally. You can do the same when painting, cleaning walls, countertops, and during another arm activity. Try to consistently use both arms and hands equally, in all directions, throughout your day.

ACTIVITY

Prevent arthritic changes by keeping your hands strong. Avoid cracking your joints. Fully open and close your fingers. Make the motions in warm water to relieve pain and stiffness and then in a bucket of rice to build strength. Lean on your hands, putting your palms flat on a table for 30 seconds, and then bend your wrists forward and backward as far as possible to build strength and range of motion. Massage yourself for pain relief and comfort. Playing an instrument, doing art or crafts, typing, handwriting neatly, and any fine handwork will keep your hands agile. Practicing all of these activities will help to keep your hands functioning and pain-free.

Lower Back and Pelvis

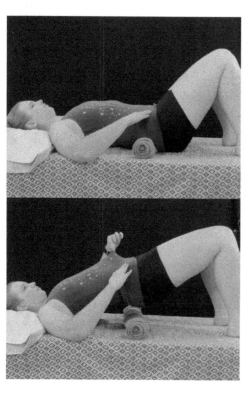

As stated previously, back pain is quite common and very subjective. Proper alignment, posture, biomechanics (alignment and leverage as you move), and ergonomics (workspace design) impact your pain and injury prevention. Literature over the last thirty years says that eight out of ten people suffer back pain. That is not surprising when you consider wide-spread poor posture in sitting, driving, computer work, hand-held devices, watching TV, etc. Correcting your postural foundation is the first step to preventing and stopping back pain. Strengthening your back and core is also important.

ACTIVITY

Bridges are a good way to build or maintain motion and strength in your low back, hips, and legs. Progress slowly. You may feel muscle cramping, so stay just under the start of a cramp. Cramping often means that the muscles are weak in that position or during that motion. Gently and consistently move into and through your limitation.

Lie on your back with a rolled towel under your low back at your waist. Bend your knees, feet flat on the floor. Lift your buttocks off the floor, keeping a neutral position in your low back (a slight inward curve) as you lift. Don't curl your bottom under and flatten your low back as you raise your buttocks. *Slowly* lift your buttocks as if your belly button is pulling you up. Lift as high as you can, keeping your knees apart, in line with your feet and pelvic bones. Don't let your knees "kiss" or fall outward. You will probably feel a pull along the front of your thighs. If you start to feel a cramp, fully straighten your leg, and pull your toes toward your head. Remember that cramping is often an indicator of muscle weakness.

Lift your buttocks as high as possible, and hold that position for up to 5 seconds. *Slowly* lower your back and buttocks to kiss the roll and lift again. Don't collapse on the floor between bridges unless you don't have the strength or feel cramps. Gradually work toward lifting and just touching the rolled towel until you can repeat it 3-30 times. Use a lumbar roll or rolled towel at your waistline when sitting to support your back and train proper posture.

Hip, Thigh and Knee

Falling is a major cause of death for older people. With good hip, back, and leg strength, you have a significantly better chance of avoiding falls and death as a result of falling. With society becoming more sedentary, losing lower body strength at any age becomes more relevant.

It is natural to avoid movement when you feel pain or apprehension. It is critical to listen carefully to your body and identify limiting problems so that you can give appropriate time and care to healing and recovery.

Do you favor and overly protect an arm, leg, or part of your spine? It is natural to subconsciously avoid using stairs if you have felt discomfort or pain in your knees or hips. By avoiding stairs, your hip and knee muscles weaken, and surrounding

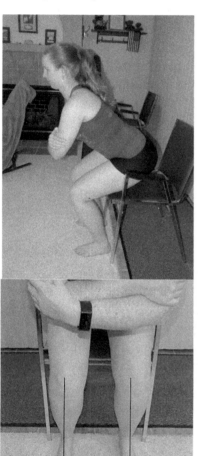

tissues may tighten due to lack of motion. Joint pain will persist and increase with disuse and progressing weakness.

Subconscious protection, or favoring, happens when one leg is weaker than the other. You may start going up and down stairs with the strong leg only. The result of favoring one leg can result in serious hip fractures and falls.

Correct problems instead of avoiding them. Ask your muscles to do all they can safely. Instead of dragging yourself upstairs by pulling, push down on the handrail slightly behind you, as you would with a cane. Lean forward as you climb, letting your legs do the work. Your hands positioned slightly behind you on the handrails will prevent your falling backward and will give your legs stability as they gain strength. Move to and through your limitations until you gain enough strength and balance to wean off your arm support. If your pain is due to muscle weakness, the pain will decrease, and your strength will increase in about 3-6 weeks of consistency. Don't give up!

ACTIVITY

One of the best things you can do to prevent falls, hip pain, and low back pain is to make a habit of "slow sit-to-stand." Watch people around you as they sit or stand up from sitting. Notice how they flop, like a sack of potatoes, and fall onto chairs, sofas, or into cars. See how they use their arms. Do they touch the chair lightly, be sure that it is there, and depend on their legs to lower and raise their body weight? Or do they lean heavily on their arms to push themselves out of the seat? The more you rely on your arms to support your weight, the more you deprive your legs of strength. We can fall into detrimental habits without knowing it.

Are your arms stealing your leg strength?

I don't like to exercise just to exercise. I want to exercise for purpose and joy. Because I want to correct problems, not only do busywork, I practice what I preach. Habitually, I align my hips, knees, and feet, and use my legs to lower and raise myself from *every* seated position—bed, chair, toilet, car, sofa, etc.

I invite you to do the same. *Safety first!* Use your arms and hands to guide you *all the way* through the motion, giving you support until your legs become strong enough to control your descent and rise. Do not jerk or lurch when standing or sitting. Slow movement requires control and balances muscle length and strength. You don't need to do this as an exercise if you make it part of your daily life. Practice *slow* sit-to-stand throughout the day by keeping your knees in line with your shoulders and pelvic bones in front. Align the center of your kneecap over your 2nd toe. Don't let your knees "kiss" as you lower or raise yourself. If your legs are weak, you will see your knees wobble together and apart as you *slowly* sit or stand. Use your hands on the seat just enough to help your knees stay aligned until your legs are strong enough to stay in alignment and lift you without arm help. Your ability to maintain your knee alignment and prevent wobbling in or out will improve as you gain strength. Generally, you will feel muscle soreness migrate along the inside of your knee to the outside of your hip as you get stronger. Use your ice, massage the sore areas, and *keep up the good work*! The soreness will cease in about 3-12 weeks. You should be able to stop and maintain alignment and balance at any part of the motion. Sit and stand like **royalty**—not like a sack of potatoes. Your knees, legs, and furniture will thank you.

If you do have knee or hip pain, degenerative changes are often reported as "bone-on-bone." That promotes fear and hopelessness in patients but doesn't change the management of the problem. Keep as much motion and strength as possible, manage pain, and watch your alignment. Your pain might diminish or, if you need surgery, you will have a more rapid and successful recovery.

Through high school and into college, I was a gymnast. When I was 16 years old, I blew out my right knee, tearing my anterior cruciate ligament (ACL), my medial meniscus (cartilage), and the medial collateral ligament (MCL). In 1967, today's surgical options were not available, so I received a de-rotation brace to stabilize my injured knee. Over the next forty years, I dealt with the progressing "bone-on-bone" arthritis by keeping my legs strong and mobile. I continued to ride and show horses, hike, swim, and be active. I massaged my knees and legs almost constantly in the car, at home, under the table at restaurants. I used ice after activity to relieve pain and used aspirin only about twice per month. "Bone-on-bone" sounds scary, but it doesn't change the need to stay active and function as fully as you can.

Finally, the osteoarthritis in my right knee was so bad that I could not bend my knees enough to sit naturally or slowly. I was having pain and difficulty walking. X-rays confirmed that arthritic bone spurs around my knee were beginning to interfere with tendon and ligament function. Total knee replacement technology had progressed in 2010 to the point that the replacements would tolerate more activity and last longer, which made me more willing to consider a replacement.

I had put off the surgery for forty-three years until there was nothing more I could do to improve my knee function. I could not sit slowly, run, hike, jump, or dance. I worked to keep my muscle strength and motion as much as possible to help my recovery from surgery and had my right knee replaced.

Some people think that having replacement surgery will solve all their pain and problems. Not so. It is wise to get pre-operative and post-operative training before having serious surgery. People had come to me thinking that they needed surgery when all they needed was correct alignment, strength, and balance training.

I have now had both knees replaced, which I hope will last the rest of my life. In 2010, I could not bend my right knee to 90-degrees to sit normally. Now, I can almost sit on both heels. It has taken a few years, but I consistently ask, without forcing, because I don't like pain. I lost about forty pounds because I could be more active. Now I can run, ride, hike, jump, and dance—without pain.

To this day, I continue to *slowly* sit↔stand, using my hands only to be sure that the seat is there, as I instruct others to do—with chairs, bed, car, in the bathroom, at home and outside the home. I also get up and down from the floor, which keeps my legs, trunk, and arms strong and flexible. That ability was especially important when our daughter was a college exchange student in Tokyo, and I toured Japan with her.

I didn't know how to shop for a good surgeon when I needed my surgery, but here are some things that could make your recovery faster and more satisfactory if you are considering surgery:

1. Shop for a surgeon that will clearly explain why you need the surgery. Review the previous Health care Shopping section. Is a total joint replacement or a partial replacement best for you? What other options are available

to solve your problems? Will the surgery need to be done again?

2. Ask your surgeon for recommendations from previous patients. Ask for evidence of his or her success rate with the surgeries of the kind you are considering.

3. Ask about the recovery—Is an ice cuff prescribed immediately after surgery? A cryocuff that surrounds the shoulder or knee with *ice and compression* is remarkably effective in relieving pain and speeding healing.

4. Ask if the hardware used will hinder post-op activity. When healed, will you be able to participate in the activities that are important to you? This was important because I wanted to bend my knees fully, hike, and jump down from rocks. If I fell, I did not want my legs injured because they wouldn't have full normal motion. My doctor assured me that I could have full motion and strength by being consistent with my IHP over time.

5. Find out how you can prepare for your surgery and recovery. Get physical therapy training before your surgery to learn how you can make your recovery faster and less painful. Do the strengthening and motion exercises before your surgery to feel the correct muscle actions to recreate them after surgery. Buy or borrow a walker (a standard pick-up walker with no wheels or skids is my preference) or a cane. Do you have ice packs ready in the freezer? It helps to meet the staff and see the rehabilitation facilities. Talk about the recovery process—before and after your surgery.

6. Allow some time before scheduling your surgery. Do the recommended post-op exercises for a while to see if they help you. At best, the alignment, strength, and motion exercises may show you that you don't need surgery now. At worst, your post-op recovery will be faster with better muscle tone and muscle memory.

Ankle and Foot

Return circulation from your lower legs is heavily dependent on muscle action. Keep dancing is good advice. Whenever you are sitting—in a car, at your desk, lounging in front of the TV, on an airplane, or at home—move your feet and toes. When you are standing, shift weight. It's easy to be still for hours when sitting or standing, but that can result in lower leg and foot swelling, pressure sores, varicose veins, and other vascular problems.

ACTIVITY

Massage your feet daily. If you live in sandals and walk barefoot, you need to take good care of your feet. Wash your feet and massage moisturizing lotion into the skin daily. Put petroleum jelly on rough heels and feet at night and wear socks to keep the ointment from rubbing off. You will be amazed how quickly the skin and the feeling in your feet improve with consistent massage and skincare.

Dancing (keeping your toes and ankles moving, weight shifting) is an excellent way to resolve foot pain and tingling. One foot can massage the other foot and lower leg when you are sitting or in bed. Use your toes to pick up things off the floor. These activities promote muscle strength, structural support, and prevent pain in your feet.

Ankle Circles/ABC's

Sit or lie down with your legs elevated comfortably. Keep your knees and thighs still as you make full, slow circles in both directions with your toes. Make sure that you move equally into all four quadrants as you make good circles. The motion should occur at the ankle, not the knee or hip. Keep your leg from rotating as you scribe the circles with your big toe. It is common to find that some parts of the circle are more challenging to draw than other parts. That means that you need to work on those areas more than the easy segments. Continue until your muscles fatigue—when you feel a burning sensation. Give yourself a good rest before repeating.

❑   Do this exercise two to three times per day, 3-20 repetitions.

ABC's: In the same position, keeping the motion in the ankles, neatly print the alphabet in the air with your toes. Carefully form all the letters with your big toe, moving your ankle only 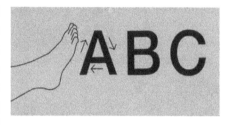 while keeping your knee and leg still. Remember what letter you were on when you felt muscle fatigue to see improvement when you pass that letter on the next attempt.

❑   Do this exercise two to three times per day.

APPENDIX

Ice Therapy for Home Use

Whenever you are injured, consider using ice immediately. It relieves pain, slows bleeding, and prevents swelling. Initial first aid until the injury is stabilized is referred to as RICE—Rest, Ice, Compress, Elevate. Gently restoring movement and function is important as soon as appropriate.

Even when you are not injured, elevating your feet helps prevent leg and foot swelling. Remember to keep dancing. Muscle activity in your feet and ankles pushes blood back up your legs toward your heart, preventing congestion, swelling, and vascular breakdown. Gentle dancing—weight shifting and foot and ankle motion—also prevents foot pain while keeping the muscles toned and supportive ligaments functioning well.

Ice and compression over and around an injury site supports broken bones, slows bleeding, and prevents swelling. For everyday aches, strains, and pains, use numbing cold to manage pain and speed healing.

Benefits of Numbing Cold

Pain Relief. Numbing cold acts to minimize pain without the internal side effects of medication. Rarely will you receive lasting relief from one application or inconsistent applications. The benefits of proper and consistent ice therapy can be miraculous. Allow enough time between ice treatments for the tissues to return to normal temperature and color—at least 60 minutes between sessions.

Circulation. Ice increases surface and deep circulation by directing blood flow to deeper tissues when applied. Then, as the skin becomes colder, blood flow is flushed to the surface to prevent the skin from freezing. This circulatory flushing effect rids tissues of waste products that can increase pain and aids the healing of deep and superficial tissues.

Muscle Spasm Stopped. Proper use of numbing cold stops muscle spasm and guarding. If you ice while practicing excellent posture and, if appropriate, use a gentle, corrected position as instructed, ice speeds the way your body learns and maintains correct positions.

Cautions. Do not use ice if you cannot feel cold or if you have circulatory problems. If you have questions about heat or cold therapy, ask your therapist or physician.

Follow these instructions:

- Set up an Ice Station that you can leave in the corner of a room where you can ice quickly and consistently.
- On the floor, place a pillow, rolled towel, and a blanket ready to go.
- Stay as comfortable as possible, and avoid chilling. Have an electric blanket available or throw a blanket in the dryer while preparing for your ice therapy.
- Position yourself and the ice correctly and then cover yourself with the blanket.
- Position your body as instructed and set the timer.
- The part on ice should be cold, but the rest of your body should be warm and comfortable. First, you will feel eye-popping cold. In about 2 minutes, your skin will feel prickly. Finally, in 7-10 minutes, you will feel fine. That's the time to get off the ice because your skin is numb and should be pink like a mild sunburn. *Avoid frostbite*!

- If frostbite does occur, the skin looks blanched (pale) and feels stiff. Warm the area slowly with your hand or warm towels. The frostbite area may sting and feel sensitive, so avoid using ice on the site until the tissue heals in about 2–4 weeks.

When you apply the ice pack, place one thickness of paper towel or a thin pillowcase between your skin and the pack. Lie down on the pack on the floor (beds and sofas are too soft) and maintain an excellent posture to hold the pack securely in good contact with your body.

- Set a timer for seven to ten minutes: It may only take one to three minutes of direct ice on the skin to achieve numbness. Be especially careful when placing ice in a plastic bag directly on the skin. Ice in contact with skin is the fastest way to frostbite. Sensitive, elderly, or damaged skin may tolerate less time. You should feel intense cold initially. In a few minutes, you should feel a burning or prickly sensation. Finally, you begin to feel okay or nothing in the area. When you start to feel "this isn't so bad" or "it's comfortable now," get off the ice! After the numbness, frostbite begins. Usually, numbness occurs within seven to fifteen minutes, so ten minutes is an average time. You can go under the ten minutes as long as you stop when your skin is pink like a mild sunburn. Avoid frostbite! You should not see any blanched areas in the pink area. Frostbite looks pale or white, and the skin feels stiff, like cardboard. Note: If this accidentally happens, warm the area with your hands or barely warm moist towels until the pink color returns. It will feel like sunburn as it heals. Minimize ice on these areas until the skin heals—usually about three weeks.
- Use ice before bed and two to three times per day (up to once per hour) to relieve pain and stop muscle spasm. If pain awakens you at night and keeps you

awake for more than ten minutes, use ice. Consistent and proper use of ice stops spasms and aids healing.

- Your job is to stay ahead of the pain.

Ice Cup Therapy

The most common reason that you do not improve with ice therapy is not using the ice frequently enough or not achieving numbing cold.

- Fill paper cups (any size you wish) with water and freeze. The paper allows you to hold the ice comfortably, and you can tear down the paper to expose the ice (which you can't do with plastic).
- Use towels to catch any drips.
- Massage the ice over the painful area for about one to three minutes. You will see the skin initially blanch and then gradually turn pink.
- Stop the ice when the area is numb and pink. Avoid frostbite!

General Use for Ice Therapy

The general rules for using ice are:

- Use ice to treat sprains, strains, and any injury where bleeding or swelling may become a problem.
- Do not use chemical rubs and pain relievers on your skin when applying heat or ice.
- If you feel a muscle spasm or soft tissue pain, try numbing cold (ice) therapy.
- If you feel sore or achy, and heat would feel good, take a warm shower followed by ice. Determine the best and longest-lasting result. Always try to end with ice.
- Use ice on muscular areas, not over skin and bone. Avoid prolonged cold on hands, feet, kneecaps, and other bony areas.

- Be extremely cautious when using ice on the elderly or people with sensitive, thin, or damaged skin.

When you use heat, do not stay in contact with the heat for more than 10–20 min. Allow at least 60 minutes between applications, and never sleep on heat or ice! (Heat can cause burns, circulatory congestion, swelling, and muscle irritability. Ice can cause frostbite.)

APPENDIX

Key Concepts for Injury Prevention

1. How you LIVE (your posture and position through your day) will influence your athletic, on the job, and at home performance. Good habits prevent pain and structural problems.

2. Degenerative joint changes will be minimized by actively monitoring and improving your structural alignment and continually working for *ideal* rather than normal. The results are worth the effort!

3. Structural correction should not be painful. It is not easy to change habits, and it will take time and consistency, but the correct positioning and movements should not be painful or cause strain. Changes in tissue length, strength, and endurance occur in small amounts over time. You will find that you will not be able to maintain major structural corrections for long (seconds, usually), so improve your posture many times throughout the day as your staying power increases. Correcting your position and movement will then become easier and finally habitual.

See videos on
4x4Healing.com.
For more specifics
on how to build a healthy habit, search for
How Can a Red Dot Improve Your Health.

4. Endurance of major muscle groups will improve with postural correction. And, as you continue to correct your position and biomechanics, you will effectively balance the length relationships of muscle and other soft tissues.

5. SET your STABILIZING FORCES (the triangle of stability for your spine, your core) before you move!! A building crane is only as good as the counter balancing force that holds the base still and allows the arm to move and lift. SET the "triangle of stability" for your trunk, shoulder, and pelvic girdle muscles in excellent alignment (chin in, shoulders down and back, lower abdominal support and gluteal muscles on) before you move your arms

or legs. This sequencing will become automatic as the strength and endurance of your trunk stabilizing muscles improves.

6. Know your own characteristics by warming up and stretching carefully, specifically, and actively to determine any limitations or problems that you might have, and so that you can improve your condition. Pay attention to target heart rate and other safety factors that are important to you as an individual.

Check out *Active Stretching*

7. It takes TIME! Don't expect results in days or a few weeks, especially when the problem may have developed over years. Bad habits do not resolve without work. Though you should start to see good changes in 2-4 weeks, consistency is the key and will pay off in a few months.

APPENDIX

Plantar Fasciitis

What is plantar fasciitis?

Plantar fasciitis (pronounced "PLAN-tar fash-ee-EYE-tus") is the most common cause of heel pain. The plantar fascia is the flat band of tissue (ligament) that connects your heel bone to your toes. It supports the arch of your foot. If you strain your plantar fascia, it gets weak, swollen, and irritated. Then your heel or the bottom of your foot hurts when you stand or walk. Physical therapy treatment, the following exercises, and ice therapy can help correct this problem.

ACTIVITY

Sitting in excellent posture, put a towel or cloth under your feet. Practice gathering the cloth with your toes, pulling the cloth under your foot. Then push the cloth away with your toes. If you feel cramping, push your heel down as you pull your toes up. Hold that position until the cramp stops. Cramping means that the muscles are weak, and you need this exercise. Do the exercise to just under the point of cramping and the cramping will eventually stop.

❏ Do this exercise two to three times per day, 10–30 repetitions each

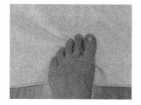 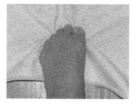 

Gripping with your toes   Pulling, gathering   Pushing towel away

On smooth surfaces or rugs, pull (gather) the cloth and push the cloth away with your toes.

Foot & Ankle Strengthening: Point your toes (like a ballet dancer) as far as you can comfortably (just under "cramping") and hold for five to ten seconds. Curl your toes at the end of each motion. If you feel cramping, pull your toes up, pushing your heel down as you pull your toes up toward your face. Rest and repeat until there are no more cramping.

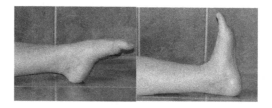

❏ Do this exercise two to five times per day, 3-20 repetitions each.

When you are able to do this without pain or problem 30 times without rest, walk on your heels about 20 to 50 feet and then on your toes for the same distance. This is also good for your balance so be sure to walk on your heels and toes in a safe area where you can hold on to a sturdy object to prevent falling.

Ice Therapy for your feet:

1. **ICE CUP THERAPY:** Fill **paper** cups (any size you wish) with water and freeze. The paper allows you to hold the ice comfortably and you can peel down the paper to expose the ice, which you can't do with plastic. Use towels to catch any drips. With your ice cup, massage firmly around your heel, especially over the sole from the heel to the arch to the base of your toes for 1 to 3 minutes until the areas are pink and numb. You will see the skin turn pale and then gradually turn pink. Avoid frostbite!

2. Fill any bottle that is corrugated or has ridges on it, with water and freeze it. Sitting in excellent posture, roll the sole of your foot on the ice-filled bottle, especially around the heel to ice massage your feet. Continue rolling the sole of your foot on the ice bottle until the sole of your foot is pink (1 to 3 minutes). Remember to avoid frostbite

 Check out *Ice Therapy for Home Use*

❏ Ice at least three to five times per day until you no longer feel pain upon standing. Then continue for two weeks after symptoms cease to assure lasting healing.

APPENDIX

Reactive or Responsive Decision-Making Steps

What steps do you take to make a decision? How do you break down a problem to solve it?

You can face a situation in one of two ways: Reactive or responsive. Reactive means the situation and outside influences control your thoughts, choices, actions, or inactions. Responsive means you are in control. You recognize the situation, the options, the goal, and you actively work through the problem.

Once you recognize a problem exists, here are seven basic steps to help make your decision:

STEP 1:
Recognize that something could be better. Determine the cause or situation to be changed. Separate fact from opinion.

STEP 2:
Develop a list of options to improve the situation. Are there other people involved who will be impacted by the problem and the correction? Do they recognize the problem also? Can they help? What are their motives and goals to solve the problem and improve the condition? What are the positive and negative impacts on you and others involved—short and long term?

STEP 3:
Ask for guidance from our Creator. Don't waste time, sweat, tears, and resources trying to grope your way through life on

your understanding and strength. Ask for help and clarity. Pain, stumbling, and traps can be avoided by turning on light when you enter a dark room filled with obstacles. The same is true in striving to handle life in your strength and understanding. It's better to have a map or guide when traveling through unknown territory.

Praying first, resting in Jesus' care, following His direction, proceeding in His strength, time, will, Word, and way significantly decreases stress.

STEP 4:

Will you be reactive? Do the chips fall where they may, and do you surrender your hope, plans, and future to external control? Or are you responsive? Do you actively use your voice and leadership skills to improve the situation with unity and management of your thoughts, emotions, and actions? Remember: no choice is a choice.

STEP 5:

Prioritize good options and reject the bad ones. Do this based on your goals, desires, available time, and resources. Factor in help from other people. If you have prayed and trust in God's control and guidance, allow for His wonderful, seemingly impossible options.

After my husband retired, he looked for a job to keep his mind and body active. We listed several conditions for an ideal job, including working virtually from home when the weather was bad or when we had a chance to travel. It didn't take long before he found a job. After the first day, he came home and, with a smile, told me he could work virtually from home some of the time. God is so good! We asked God for what was beyond our grasp and saw God's blessings!

STEP 6:

Choose the most favorable option from your revised list and make a plan. What is the best, or necessary, timing? What resources do you need to accomplish the change? How will you exercise options to change the problem or situation? Will these changes benefit or harm you or others? What do you expect when the situation is corrected? If your expectations do not occur, what is the worst thing that can happen? What will your life look like when the problem is fixed or improved?

STEP 7:

To the best of your ability, prevent negative results when you take action. According to your plan, acquire the necessary resources, information, and help. Then prepare. Do what you can do to make the best of the situation. Take the first step and continue to the goal.

Use some or all of these seven steps to help you practice O-C-A intentionally through your day. Get help if you have difficulty seeing options and the possible positive and negative results of those options.

APPENDIX
Your Reticular Activating System (RAS)

The cycle of thought-message-action reinforcement is well-researched.[81, 82] You've seen your reticular activating system (RAS) in action. This bundle of neurons in your brain stem is an amazing area of the non-cognitive brain that protects you from being overwhelmed by the millions of messages you receive every day through sight, sound, touch, and taste. Smell inputs do not go immediately to the RAS. Information we collect through smell travels to the emotional center of the brain.

These specialized RAS nerves filter out extraneous information to focus on what is important to you. As the RAS sifts through the enormous amount of information bombarding you every day, it looks for threat indicators. Your RAS focuses on what will help you function and information that supports your safety, and what you believe, desire, and value.

Here's how your RAS filter works. In a large crowd, you tune in to your name but ignore the other voices and noise. When shopping for a certain kind or color of a car, you see more of that car and color than you ever noticed before. If you like animals, art, shopping malls, houses for sale, etc., those objects pop out while you ignore surrounding images and sounds.

Your RAS filter reinforces your perspective. A grumbling, complaining, and pessimistic outlook invites experiences and information that strengthen those attitudes and beliefs. If you believe you can't, you're correct. If you believe this will be a bad day, your RAS filter focuses on all the delays, troubles, and frustrations during the day.

On the other hand, if you choose to fill your mind with helpful *truths* about yourself, your RAS filter seeks confirming evidence. It is not wishful thinking—your RAS operates on reality. When you identify encouraging facts about yourself or the situation, you think, decide, and function more effectively in relationships, at work, in sports, through the day. You have a better outlook through whatever happens. Your positive experiences reinforce constructive messages, thoughts, and beliefs. As beneficial results transform negative feelings into positive ones, you experience healing.

Choose to activate your RAS filter to build resiliency and contentment.

ENDNOTES

1   The Journal of the American Osteopathic Association, April 2009, Vol. 109, 229-233.

2   http://www.naasca.org/2012-Resources/010812-StaisticsOfChildAbuse.htm

3   https://www.nsvrc.org/statistics#:~:text=The%20 self%2Dreported%20incidence%20of,the%20United%20 States%20in%202018 – Child Sexual Abuse - Accessed September 29, 2019

4   www.ndvh.org. "The Domestic Violence Hotline: Hotline Reports 15 Percent Increase" (2005). http://www.ndvh.org/ press/index.php. (accessed October 5, 2019).

5   https://www.healthline.com/health/wolffs-law; *How Your Workout Strengthens Your Bones*; Medically reviewed by William Morrison, M.D. — Written by Jill Seladi-Schulman, Ph.D. on January 28, 2019. (accessed October 7, 2019).

6   Soltan, Liz. "Taking Control of Your Digital Life." DigitalResponsibility.org. http://www.digitalresponsibility. org/health-and-technology (accessed November 25, 2019).

7   Twenge, Jean M., PhD. "Incidents in Depression, Self-Harm, and Suicide Among U.S. Adolescents After 2012

and Links to Technology Use—Possible Mechanisms." prcp.
psychiatryonline.org. https://prcp.psychiatryonline.org/doi/
full/10.1176/appi.prcp.20190015 (accessed October 10, 2019).

8   Pogosyan, Marianna, Ph.D. "Positive Emotions and
Wellbeing." PsychologyToday.com. https://www.
psychologytoday.com/us/blog/between-cultures/201611/
positive-emotions-and-wellbeing. (accessed October 10, 2019).

Cohen, Rachel. "Physical Pain is in Sync with Emotional
Pain." SouthwestSpineandPain.com.

https://www.southwestspineandpain.com/blog/physical-
pain-sync-emotional-pain (accessed October 9, 2019).

9   Health24.com. "How Deep Sleep Could Rinse The Day's
Toxins From The Brain". https://www.health24.com/Medical/
Sleep/News/how-deep-sleep-could-rinse-the-days-toxins-
from-brain-20191107-2 (accessed October 10, 2019.)

10   Davis, Charles Patrick, M.D., Ph.D. "How Can You
Prevent Fatigue?" EMedicineHealth.com. https://www.
emedicinehealth.com/fatigue/article_em.htm#how_can_you_
prevent_fatigue (accessed 10/10/2019).

11   Johns, Murray, M.D. "About the ESS."
EpworthSleepinessScale.com. https://epworthsleepinessscale.
com/about-the-ess/ (accessed October 10, 2019).

12   Wilder, E. James, Edward M. Khouri, Chris M. Coursey,
Sheila D. Sutton. "JOY Starts Here: the transformation zone".
(Lexington: Shepherd's House, Inc., 2013), pg. 7-8, 17-20.

13   Van Der Kolk, Bessel, M.D. "The Body Keeps the Score—
Brain, Mind, and Body in the Healing of Trauma". (New
York: Penguin Books, 2015), pg. 20-21.

14   Van Der Kolk, Bessel, M.D. "The Body Keeps the Score—
Brain, Mind, and Body in the Healing of Trauma". (New
York: Penguin Books, 2015), pg. 51-73.

15   Shore, Allan N. "Affect Regulation and the Repair of the
Self". (New York/London: W.W. Norton & Co., Inc., 2003),
pg. 7-10, Fig.A-7

16   *Bonding and the Treatment of Dissociation.* DVD. 2008.
Directed by Jim Wilder, Ph.D. Originally Released July 1,

2008. Lexington: Shepherd's House, 2008) LifeModel.org. https://www.LifeModel.org/product.php?type=video&rn=66

17 Van Der Kolk, Bessel, M.D. "The Body Keeps the Score—Brain, Mind, and Body in the Healing of Trauma". (New York: Penguin Books, 2015), pg. 80-87.

18 Wilder, E. James, Edward M. Khouri, Chris M. Coursey, Sheila D. Sutton. "JOY Starts Here: the transformation zone". (Lexington: Shepherd's House, Inc., 2013), pg. 19-21.

19 Krockow, Eva M., Ph.D. "How Many Decisions Do We Make Each Day?" PsychologyToday.com. https://www.psychologytoday.com/us/blog/stretching-theory/201809/how-many-decisions-do-we-make-each-day (accessed November 14, 2019).

20 John 8:44

21 Psalm 14:1-3, 22; Isaiah 53, 9:6; Micah 5:2; Romans 3:23, 6:23, 5:8, 10:9-10

22 Lawson, Karen, M.D. "How Do Thoughts and Emotions Affect Health?" takingcharge.csh.umn.edu. https://www.takingcharge.csh.umn.edu/how-do-thoughts-and-emotions-affect-health (accessed October 25, 2019).

23 Eareckson Tada, Joni. "Why Joni Eareckson Tada Praises God For Not Healing Her." TheGospelCoalition.org. https://www.thegospelcoalition.org/article/joni-earekson-tada-praises-healing (accessed November 14, 2019).

24 Jeremiah 29:11-13

25 Mayo Clinic Staff. "How to Be Happy: Tips for Cultivating Contentment." MayoClinic.org. https://www.mayoclinic.org/healthy-lifestyle/stress-management/in-depth/how-to-be-happy/art-20045714 (accessed January 10, 2020).

26 Siegel, Daniel J., M.D. The Developing Mind—How Relationships and the Brain Interact to Shape Who We Are. 2nd Edition. (New York: Guilford Press, 2015), pg. 147-148.

27 Siegel, Daniel J., M.D. The Developing Mind—How Relationships and the Brain Interact to Shape Who We Are. 2nd Edition. (New York: Guilford Press, 2015), pg. 147-148.

28   Siegel, Daniel J., M.D. The Developing Mind—How Relationships and the Brain Interact to Shape Who We Are. 2nd Edition. (New York: Guilford Press, 2015), pg. 148.

29   Cohen, Rachel. "Physical Pain is in Sync with Emotional Pain." SouthwestSpineandPain.com. https://www.southwestspineandpain.com/blog/physical-pain-sync-emotional-pain (accessed October 10, 2019).

30   Ong, Anthony D., Daniel K. Mroczek, Catherine Riffin. "The Health Significance of Positive Emotions in Adulthood and Later Life." NlmNih.gov. https://www.ncbi.nlm.nih.gov/pmc/articles/PMC3173764/ (accessed October 13, 2019).

31   https://www.psychologytoday.com/us/blog/imperfect-spirituality/201902/why-hope-matters (accessed October 14, 2019).

32   Goodman, Catherine C., MBA PT CBP. Pathology: Implications for the Physical Therapist. 3rd Edition. (St. Louis: WB Saunders Co., 2008), pg. 65.

33   Szalavitz, Maia. "Touching Empathy." PsychologyToday.com https://www.psychologytoday.com/us/blog/born-love/201003/touching-empathy (accessed December 10, 2019).

34   Farber, Sharon K., Ph.D. "Why We All Need To Touch and Be Touched." PsychologyToday.com https://www.psychologytoday.com/us/blog/the-mind-body-connection/201309/why-we-all-need-touch-and-be-touched (accessed December 10, 2019).

35   Mineo, Liz. "Good Genes Are Nice, But Joy Is Better." News.harvard.edu. https://news.harvard.edu/gazette/story/2017/04/over-nearly-80-years-harvard-study-has-been-showing-how-to-live-a-healthy-and-happy-life/ (accessed January 10, 2019).

36   Floyd, Kory, Ph.D. "What Lack of Affection Can Do To You." PsychologyToday.com https://www.psychologytoday.com/us/blog/affectionado/201308/what-lack-affection-can-do-you (accessed January 11, 2019).

37   Siegel, Daniel J., M.D. The Developing Mind—How Relationships and the Brain Interact to Shape Who We Are. 2nd Edition. (New York: Guilford Press, 2015), 146-148.

38   Mayo Clinic Staff. MayoClinic.org. "Positive Thinking: Stop Negative Self-Talk to Reduce Stress." https://www.mayoclinic.

org/healthy-lifestyle/stress-management/in-depth/positive-thinking/art-20043950 (accessed November 4, 2019).

39 Johns Hopkins Staff. "The Power of Positive Thinking." HopkinsMedicine.org https://www.hopkinsmedicine.org/health/wellness-and-prevention/the-power-of-positive-thinking (accessed November 4, 2019).

40 Proverbs 18:20-21

41 Bailey, Kasee. "Five Powerful Health Benefits of Journaling." Intermountainhealth care.org https://intermountainhealth care.org/blogs/topics/live-well/2018/07/5-powerful-health-benefits-of-journaling/ (accessed March 12, 2020).

42 Grate, Rachel. "Science Shows Something Surprising About People Who Still Journal." Mic.com. https://www.mic.com/articles/110662/science-shows-something-surprising-about-people-who-still-journal#.n0QO5ApTN (accessed March 12, 2020).

43 Bailey, Kasee. "Five Powerful Health Benefits of Journaling." Intermountainhealth care.org https://intermountainhealth care.org/blogs/topics/live-well/2018/07/5-powerful-health-benefits-of-journaling/ (accessed March 12, 2020).

44 Ezekiel 18:20; Romans 6:23

45 Jeremiah 29:11-13; Psalm 16:11; Matthew 17:5; John 15:11

46 Psalm 14:1-3; Isaiah 53:6; John 3:16-17; Romans 3:23, 6:23

47 2 Peter 3:9; Psalm 86:15; John 3:16-17; Isaiah 30:18; 1 Timothy 2:3-5

48 1 Corinthians 15:6

49 Psalm 2:7, 49:9; Acts 13:28-35

50 Isaiah 53:6; Romans 5:8

51 Galatians 5:1; 1 John 1:9; James 5:16

52 Psalm 14:1-3, Romans 3:23; John 3:16-17

53 Romans 6:23

54 1 John 1:9; James 5:16

55 Job16-12; Matthew 8:28-32; Luke 8:26-33

56 John 10:10

57 John 15:4-5,11; Ephesians 2:8-10

58 1 John 4:18

59 John 14:66

60   Luke 23:34; Matthew 5:44

61   Psalm 119:9-11; 2 Timothy 2:22

62   Psalm 9:10, 37:5; 2 Chronicles 20:5-25; Ephesians 3:14-21

63   Luke 5:16; Ephesians 1:18; Hebrews 13:20-21

64   Psalm 142:3; 2 Corinthians 2:7

65   Psalm 18:49; Colossians 2:6-7; Hebrews 13:15

66   Psalm 32:1; Matthew 6:12, 14; Luke 23:34

67   Matthew 6:12-15

68   John 3:16-18

69   Author Unknown, as told by Paul Harvey. "The Man and The Birds." manandthebirds.com. https://www.manandthebirds.com (accessed November 5, 2019).

70   John 3:6; Psalm 51:10; John 3:16-17

71   Romans 3:23, 6:23

72   John 1:29; Mark 3:11; John 14:6

73   Acts 3:15; 1 Corinthians 15:6; John 21:14

74   Romans 5:8, 10:9; Hebrews 11:6; Colossians 1:10

75   Psalm 136:23-24; 1 John 1:9; John 1:12

76   2 Peter 3:17-18

77   Joshua 1:9; Deuteronomy 31:6,8; Matthew 28:19-20

78   Isaiah 40:8; Hebrews 4:12; Matthew 24:35; Isaiah 55:11; Hosea 4:6; Matthew 4:4; 2 Timothy 3:16; Psalm 12:6

79   Van Der Kolk, Bessel, M.D. "The Body Keeps the Score— Brain, Mind, and Body in the Healing of Trauma". (New York: Penguin Books, 2015), pg. 60-63.

80   Van Der Kolk, Bessel, M.D. "The Body Keeps the Score— Brain, Mind, and Body in the Healing of Trauma". (New York: Penguin Books, 2015), pg. 205-206.

81   Siegel, Daniel J., M.D. *The Developing Mind—How Relationships and the Brain Interact to Shape Who We Are*. 2nd Edition. (New York: Guilford Press, 2015), pp. 10, 146-148, 157-158.

82   Jantz, Gregory L., Ph.D. "The Power of Positive Self-Talk." PsychologyToday.com. https://www.psychologytoday.com/us/blog/hope-relationships/201605/the-power-positive-self-talk (accessed November 15, 2019).

HELPFUL RESOURCES

- The Holy Bible
- Online Bible and Resources: blueletterbible.org/
- Bible Questions? gotquestions.org/
- Grace to You—John MacArthur: gty.org
- Food for Your Soul—D. Richard Ferguson: treasuringgod.com/
- Gospel of John by Waxer Tipton: vimeo.com/46461957, vimeo.com/46923224
- Desiring God—John Piper: desiringgod.org/
- Insight for Living—Chuck Swindoll: insight.org/
- *The Body Keeps the Score—Brain, Mind, and Body in the Healing of Trauma* by Bessel Van Der Kolk, MD; 2015; Penguin Books, New York, NY 10014
- *The Developing Mind—How Relationships and the Brain Interact to Shape Who We Are* by Daniel J. Siegel; 2015; The Guilford Press; New York, NY10001
- *Is It My Fault? Hope and Healing for Those Suffering Domestic Violence* by Justin S. Holcomb and Lindsey A Holcomb; 2014; Moody Publishers, Chicago, IL 60610
- *Pathology—Implications for the Physical Therapist* – 3rd Edition by by Catherine Goodman & Kenda Fuller; Saunders/Elsevier; 2009

- *Cold-Case Christianity: A Homicide Detective Investigates the Claims of the Gospels* by J. Warner Wallace; 2013; David C. Cook, 1st edition; Colorado Springs, CO 80918
- *The Case for Christ: A Journalist's Personal Investigation of the Evidence for Jesus* by Lee Strobel; 1998; Zondervan; Grand Rapids, MI 49530

ACKNOWLEDGMENTS

So many people touch and add to the quality and production of a book. This book has that strong, rich heritage.

With deepest gratitude, I thank the following:

My precious family for their patient love, understanding, and strength through this process.

My wonderful patients who chose not to settle but stepped out in courage to be the best they could be and allowed me the privilege of journeying with them.

Faithful friends across the country who gave time and valuable insights and Author Academy Elite for the coaching, resources, and direction that made this book possible.

Kirsten Samuel for her talent and hard work in editing and supporting the completion of this work. I so appreciate her heart, insights, efficiency, and guidance.

Sara Plott (Fadooger Communications) for her comprehensive care, wisdom, heart, and creative talent in getting the word out—to touch hearts and motivate positive change.

Dr. D. Richard Ferguson for his in-depth Biblical wisdom, time, support, and focus on the Source of healing. "... love the Lord your God with all your heart, with all your soul, with all your strength, and with all your mind; and your neighbor as yourself." *Luke 10:27-28*

Most of all, I thank our Creator and our Savior, the Lord Jesus Christ, the Source of Life, the ultimate Healer, and He provided everything needed to do this work.

ABOUT THE AUTHOR

Bonnie Yost, PT is a registered physical therapist, author, and speaker since 1978. She has an extensive background in manual therapy, orthopedic, sport, ob-gyn evaluation, and treatment. Her experience also includes successfully treating the effects of abuse and trauma by incorporating Biblical life-skills training while addressing wounds of the heart (emotions), mind (cognition), spirit (belief system), and body (physical condition). Mrs. Yost emphasizes practical, experiential, and functional approaches to training and treatment.

Bonnie is passionate about helping people live God's truth. She is the founder of Be Your Best (BYB) and 4x4 Healing. She has contributed to the physical therapy textbook,

Pathology—Implications for the Physical Therapist and has written small group/Bible study workbooks. She has taught nationally and internationally. Her presentations are dynamic and experiential.

Connect with Bonnie

Website: 4x4Healing.com

Facebook: 4X4Healing

YouTube: 4X4Healing

CPSIA information can be obtained
at www.ICGtesting.com
Printed in the USA
LVHW080537290321
682788LV00002B/68

9 781647 465872